CW00429274

Classic Rock

Published by
Wise Publications
14-15 Berners Street,
London W1T 3LJ, UK.

Exclusive Distributors:
Music Sales Limited
Distribution Centre,
Newmarket Road, Bury St Edmunds,
Suffolk IP33 3YB, UK.
Music Sales Pty Limited
20 Resolution Drive, Caringbah,
NSW 2229, Australia.

Order No. AM997337
ISBN 978-1-84938-079-9

This book © Copyright 2010
Wise Publications, a division of
Music Sales Limited.

Unauthorised reproduction of any part
of this publication by any means including
photocopying is an infringement of copyright.

Compiled by Nick Crispin.
Text by Graham Vickers.
Picture research by Jacqui Black.
Photographs courtesy of LFI.
Music engraved by Paul Ewers Music Design.
Music edited by Adrian Hopkins.
Design by Fresh Lemon.

www.musicsales.com

Printed in Thailand.

Wise Publications
part of The Music Sales Group
London/New York/Paris/Sydney/Copenhagen/Berlin/Tokyo/Madrid

Introduction

The GigBook: Classic Rock has something for everybody who ever dreamed of standing centre stage and wowing an audience.

This collection of rock songs illustrates pretty much every possible variation of the genre, so if you're not quite ready to launch into an atmospheric D-I-Y version of 'Hey Joe' or a window-rattling interpretation of 'Born To Be Wild', don't worry – there's still a wealth of other stuff reflecting just about every stage of the phenomenon that started with rock 'n' roll and went on to spawn various sub-genres including blues-rock, folk-rock, soft-rock, glam-rock and progressive rock.

From the pioneering days of Chuck Berry, Little Richard and Buddy Holly through the country rock of The Byrds and Creedence Clearwater Revival to hits from recent bands like Snow Patrol and Kings of Leon, rock proved itself to have considerably more lasting appeal than almost anybody predicted. When teenage audiences tore up cinema seats at 1955 screenings of 'The Blackboard Jungle', quaintly whipped into a frenzy by the revolutionary sound of 30-year old Bill Haley, an ex-Western Swing musician and yodeller, rock looked like a temporary craze. The song in question was 'Rock Around The Clock' and it set an unstoppable ball rolling. True, the kids had to turn to Elvis Presley to get an authentic rock pin-up, but Haley's records (including 'Shake, Rattle And Roll', featured here) made rock famous and soon it had a thousand disciples. In the end it was probably the music's adaptability that guaranteed its longevity. Rock served Crosby, Stills and Nash well when their brand of West Coast hippie rock came along and it inspired The Beatles. Years later New York's Blondie and London's Elvis Costello could also safely be called rock acts despite having very different musical agendas.

Particularly welcome is the inclusion of The Rolling Stones' 'Tumbling Dice', a great rock song that suffered, like the rest of the album it was featured on, from a muddy mix that made the lyrics pretty well impossible to decipher. But here they are, along with the full lyric of Dire Straits' mini-band documentary 'Sultans Of Swing' and the staccato sound-bites of 'Teenage Kicks' by The Undertones, John Peel's all-time favourite record that was played for him one last time at his funeral.

On a lighter note, rock, of course, isn't obliged to be anything but a feel-good sound, and this is a principle that was not lost on The Beach Boys while more or less exclusively underpinning the careers of bands like Slade and Status Quo. Born in the USA, rock would be enthusiastically adopted everywhere but was made especially welcome in Britain where The Beatles, The Kinks and The Who showed just how adaptable it was. Rock was to provide the soundtrack for the lives of millions of people born since the mid-20th century. Today it sounds both borderless and timeless, but, as Mott The Hoople once reminded us, rock came all the way from Memphis. It travelled well. And now you can join in.

Chuck Berry

100 HITS

All Right Now

Words & Music by Paul Rodgers & Andy Fraser

© Copyright 1970 Blue Mountain Music Limited.
All Rights Reserved. International Copyright Secured.

6

Verse 2:

I took her home to my place
Watchin' every move on her face
She said "Look, what's your game, baby?
Are you try'n' to put me in shame?"

I said-a, "Slow, don't go so fast,
Don't you think that love can last?"
She said, "Love, Lord above,
Now you're try'n' to trick me in love."

7

All The Young Dudes

Words & Music by David Bowie

© Copyright 1972 Tintoretto Music/RZO Music Limited (37.5%)/EMI Music Publishing Limited (37.5%)/Chrysalis Music Limited (25%).
All Rights Reserved. International Copyright Secured.

1. Well Bil - ly rapped all night a - bout his su - i - cide,— how he'd
(Verse 2 see block lyrics)

kick it in the head when he was twen-ty - five. Speed jive. Don't wan-na stay a - live,

when you're twen-ty - five. And Wen-dy's steal-ing clothes from Marks and Sparks, and

Fred-dy's got spots from rip-ping off the stars from his face. Fun-ky lit-tle

boat race. The tel-e-vis-ion man is cra - zy say-ing we're juv-

- en-ile del-in-quent wrecks. Oh,— Man I need a T. V.—when I got

8

T. Rex. Oh broth-er you guessed, I'm a dude_ dad.__

All the young dudes__ car-ry the news.__ Boog-a-loo dudes__

_____ car-ry the news.____ All the young dudes_

___ car-ry the news.__ Boog-a-loo dudes_____ car-ry the news.

1. ___ 2. Now ___ **2.** All the young dudes__

___ car-ry the news.__ Boog-a-loo dudes___ car-ry the news.__

Verse 2:
Now Lucy's looking sweet 'cause he dresses like a queen
But he can kick like a mule, it's a real mean team
But we can love, oh yes, we can love
And my brother's back at home with his Beatles and his Stones
We never got it off on that revolution stuff
What a drag; too many snags
Well I drunk a lot of wine and I'm feeling fine
Gonna race some cat to bed
Oh, is there concrete all around or is it in my head?
Yeah, I'm a dude dad.

9

American Girl

Words & Music by Tom Petty

© Copyright 1976 Almo Music Corporation, USA.
Rondor Music (London) Limited.
All rights in Germany administered by Rondor Musikverlag GmbH.
All Rights Reserved. International Copyright Secured.

1. Well, she was an Am - er - i - can girl, raised on pro - mi - ses.
(Verse 2 see block lyrics)

She could-n't help think-ing that there was a lit-tle more to life some - where else.

Af-ter all, it was a great big world with lots of pla-ces to run to.

And if she had to die try - ing, she had one lit-tle pro - mise she was gon-na keep.

Oh, yeah. All right. Take it ea-sy ba-by, make it last all night.

Verse 2:
Well, it was kinda cold at night
She stood alone on her balcony
Yeah, she could hear the cars roll by
Out on Four Forty-One
Like waves crashing on the beach
And for one desperate moment there
He crept back in her memory
God, it's so painful, something that's so close
And still so far out of reach.

American Pie

Words & Music by Don McLean

© Copyright 1971 Mayday Music, USA.
Universal/MCA Music Limited.
All rights in Germany administered by Universal/MCA Music Publ. GmbH.
All Rights Reserved. International Copyright Secured.

1. A long, long time a-go____ I can still re-mem-ber how that mu-sic used to make me smile.____ And I knew if I had my chance that I could make those peo-ple dance and may-be they'd be hap-py for a while. But Feb-ru-ar-y made me shi-ver with ev-'ry pa-per I'd de-liv-er. Bad news on the door-step I could-n't take one more step, I can't re-mem-ber if I cried when I read a-bout his wid-owed bride. Some-thing touched me deep in-side____ the day the mu-sic died. So

♩ = 100

bye - bye, Miss A - mer - i - can Pie,__ drove my Che - vy to the lev - ee but the

lev - ee was dry.__ Them good ole boys__ were drink - in' whis - ky and rye__ sing - in'

To Coda ⊕

this - 'll be the day__ that I__ die. This - 'll be the day__ that I__ die.__

grad. accel.

♩ = 141

2. Did you__ write the book of love__ and do you__ have faith in God a - bove?

(Verses 3-5 see block lyrics)

If the Bi - ble tells__ you so.__ Now do you__ be - lieve__ in

rock and roll,__ can mu - sic save your mor - tal soul__ and can you teach me

how to dance__ real slow?__ Well, I

13

this - 'll be the day___ that I___ die.___

Freely

6. I met a girl who sang_ the blues___ and I asked her for some hap-py news,___ but

she just smiled and turned a - way.___ I went down to the sa-cred store___where I'd

heard the mu-sic years be-fore. But the man there said the mu-sic would-n't play.____ And

in the streets the chil-dren screamed, the lov-ers cried_ and the po-ets dreamed._ But

not a word was spo-ken the church bells all were bro-ken. And the three men I ad-mire most, the

Fa-ther, Son and the Ho-ly Ghost, they caught the last train for the coast the day the mu - sic

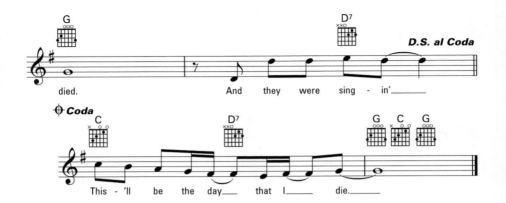

died. And they were sing - in'_____

This - 'll be the day___ that I___ die.___

Verse 3:
Now for ten years we've been on our own, and moss grows fat on a rollin' stone
But that's not how it used to be when the jester sang for the king and queen
In a coat he borrowed from James Dean and a voice that came from you and me
Oh, and while the king was looking down, the jester stole his thorny crown
The courtroom was adjourned, no verdict was returned
And while Lenin read a book on Marx, the quartet practiced in the park
And we sang dirges in the dark
The day the music died.

Verse 4:
Helter skelter in a summer swelter the birds flew off with a fallout shelter
Eight miles high and fallin' fast, it landed foul on the grass
The players tried for a forward pass, with the jester on the sidelines in a cast
Now the half-time air was sweet perfume while the sergeants played a marching tune
Oh, we all got up to dance but we never got the chance
'Cause the players tried to take the field, the marching band refused to yield
Do you recall what was revealed
The day the music died?

Verse 5:
And there we were all in one place, a generation lost in space
With no time left to start again
So come on Jack be nimble, Jack be quick! Jack flash sat on a candlestick
'Cause fire is the devil's only friend.
And as I watched him on the stage my hands were clenched in fists of rage
No angel born in hell could break that Satan's spell
And as the flames climbed high into the night to light the sacrificial rite
I saw Satan laughing with delight
The day the music died.

Are You Gonna Be My Girl

Words & Music by Nic Cester & Cameron Muncey

© Copyright 2003 Get Jet Music Incorporated.
Famous Music Publishing Limited.
All Rights Reserved. International Copyright Secured.

1,2. So one two three, take my hand and come with me be - cause you

look so fine that I real - ly wan-na make you mine.___ I said you

look so fine that I real - ly wan-na make you mine.___ A -

-four five six, come on___ and get your kicks, now you

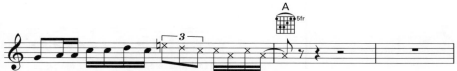

don't need a-mon-ey when you look like that, do you hon-ey?___

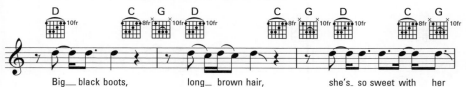

Big__ black boots, long__ brown hair, she's__ so sweet with her

American Woman

Words & Music by Randy Bachman, Burton Cummings, Jim Kale & Garry Peterson

© Copyright 1970 Shillelagh America Music, USA.
Bug Music Limited.
All Rights Reserved. International Copyright Secured.

Outro:
Go! I want to fly away
I'm gonna leave you woman*(x4)*
A-bye-bye*(x4)*
You're no good for me
And I'm no good for you
I look you right straight in the eye

I tell you what I'm gonna do
I'm gonna leave you woman
You know I got to go
I'm gonna leave you woman
I got to go*(x3)*
American woman, yeah.

Barracuda

Words & Music by Ann Wilson, Nancy Wilson, Roger Fisher & Michael DeRosier

© Copyright 1977 BMG Songs Incorporated/Strange Euphoria Music/Sheer Music/Of The Roses Music, USA.
Universal/MCA Music Limited (70%)/Universal Music Publishing MGB Limited (30%).
All rights in Germany administered by Universal/MCA Music Publ. GmbH and Musik Edition Discoton GmbH.
All Rights Reserved. International Copyright Secured.

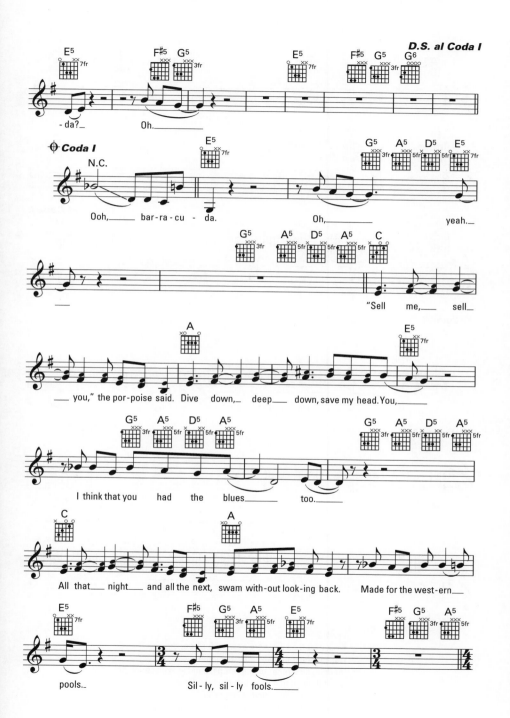

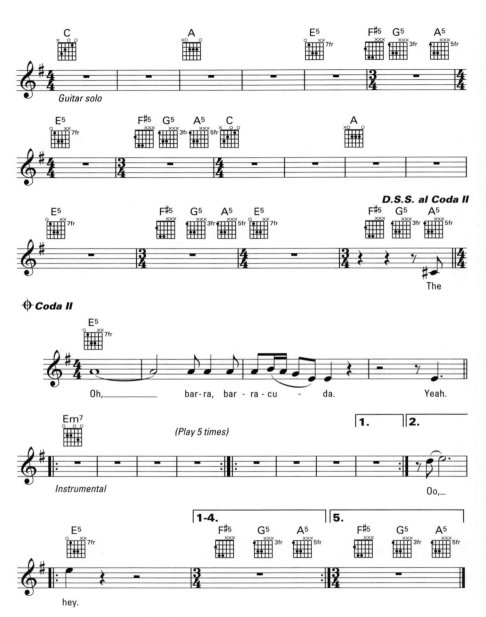

Beds Are Burning

Midnight Oil's 1987 hit can fairly claim to be a highly influential political anthem – not to mention a surprisingly adaptable one. The Australian group's musical plea on behalf of a small group of Aboriginals who had suffered displacement from their home territory was originally intended to be the apology so conspicuously unforthcoming from the Australian government of the time. Much covered over the years, the song was revived in 2009 by an assemblage of celebrities on behalf of The Global Humanitarian Forum, this time to raise awareness of global warming. The caring supergroup included Desmond Tutu, Bob Geldof, Marion Cotillard, Kofi Annan and Simon Le Bon.

Beds Are Burning

Words & Music by Peter Garrett, Robert Hirst & James Moginie

© Copyright 1988 Sprint Music
Sony/ATV Music Publishing(UK) Limited.
All Rights Reserved. International Copyright Secured.

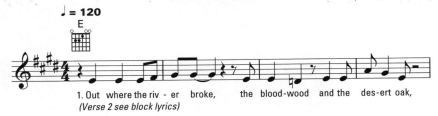

1. Out where the riv - er broke, the blood-wood and the des-ert oak,
(Verse 2 see block lyrics)

Hol-den wrecks and boil-ing die-sels, steam-ing for - ty five_ de-grees. The

time has come, to say fair's fair; to pay the rent;

to pay our share. The time has come: a

fact's a fact,_ it be-longs to them, let's

(1° only)

give it back._

give it back.__

(Drum fill)

How can we dance__ when our earth is turn - ing?

How do we sleep__ while our beds are burn - ing?__

__ How can we dance__ when our

earth is turn - ing? How do we sleep_ while our

beds are burn - ing?_____ The

29

time has come   to   say fair's fair;   to   pay   the rent__ now,   to

pay our   share.

Coda

pay our   share.   The   time   has come   a   fact's   a   fact,__   It be-

- longs   to   them,__   we've got - ta   give   it   back.__

How can we   dance when   our   earth   is   turn - ing?

How do we   sleep while   our   beds   are   burn - ing?

Verse 3:
Four wheels scare the cockatoos
From Kintore East to Yuendemu
The western desert lives and breathes
In forty-five degrees.

Centerfold

Words & Music by Seth Justman

© Copyright 1981 Center City Music/Pal-Park Music, USA.
Universal Music Publishing Limited (25%)/IQ Music Limited (75%).
All rights in Germany administered by Universal Music Publ. GmbH.
All Rights Reserved. International Copyright Secured.

1. Does she walk? Does she talk?_ Does she come com-plete? My
(Verse 2 see block lyrics)

home-room, home-room an-gel al-ways pulled me from my seat. She was pure like snow-flakes; no

one could ev-er stain the mem-o-ry of my an-gel, could nev-er cause me pain. The

years go by, I'm look-in' through a girl-ie ma-ga-zine, and there's my home-room an-gel on the

pa-ges in be-tween. My blood runs cold;_ my me-mo-ry___ has just been sold. My

an-gel is the cen-ter-fold. An-gel is the cen-ter-fold. My blood runs cold;_ my

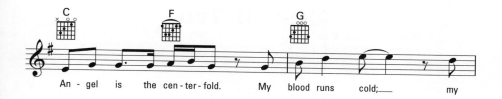

An - gel is the cen - ter - fold. My blood runs cold;___ my

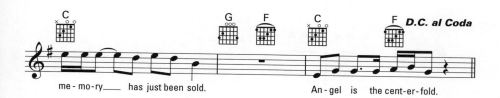

me - mo - ry___ has just been sold. An - gel is the cent-er-fold.

D.C. al Coda

⊕ Coda

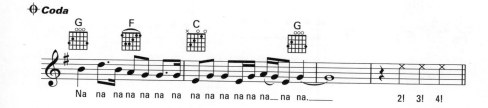

Na na na na na na na na na na na na na___ na na.___ 2! 3! 4!

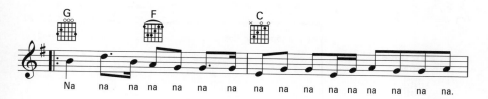

Na na na na na na na na na na na na na na na na.

Repeat to fade

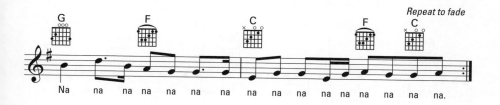

Na na na na na na na na na na na na na na na na.

Verse 2:
It's okay, I understand, this ain't no never never land
I hope that when this issue's gone, I'll see you when your clothes are on
Take your car, yes, we will, we'll take your car and drive it
We'll take it to a motel room and take 'em off in private
A part of me has just been ripped, the pages from my mind are stripped
Ah no! I can't deny it. Oh yeah, I guess I gotta buy it.

33

Best Of You

Words & Music by Dave Grohl, Taylor Hawkins, Nate Mendel & Chris Shiflett

© Copyright 2005 Songs Of Universal Incorporated/M.J.-Twelve Music/Living Under A Rock Music/I Love The Punk Rock Music, USA.
Flying Earform Music (BMI) administered by Bug Music Limited (12.5%)/Universal/MCA Music Limited (87.5%)
(administered in Germany by Universal/MCA Music Publ. GmbH).
All Rights Reserved. International Copyright Secured.

34

35

Verse 3:
My heart is under arrest again
But I break loose
My head is giving me life or death
But I can't choose
I swear I'll never give in, I refuse.

Verse 4:
I got another confession my friend
I'm no fool
I'm getting tired of starting again
Somewhere new.

37

Black Hole Sun

Words & Music by Chris Cornell

© Copyright 1994 You Make Me Sick I Make Music, USA.
Universal/MCA Music Limited.
All rights in Germany administered by Universal/MCA Music Publ. GmbH.
All Rights Reserved. International Copyright Secured.

Original key: A♭. To match original recording, tune down one semitone.

Verse 2:
Stuttering, cold and damp
Steal the warm wind tired friend
Times are gone for honest men
Sometimes far too long for snakes

In my shoes, a walking sleep
And my youth I pray to keep
Heaven send hell away
No one sings like you anymore.

Born To Be Wild

Words & Music by Mars Bonfire

© Copyright 1968 Manitou Music, USA.
Universal/MCA Music Limited.
All rights in Germany administered by Universal/MCA Music Publ. GmbH.
All Rights Reserved. International Copyright Secured.

♩ = 146

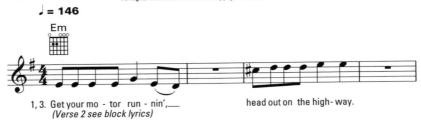

1, 3. Get your mo - tor run - nin',___ head out on the high- way.
(Verse 2 see block lyrics)

look - ing for ad - ven - ture, and what - ev - er comes our___ way.___

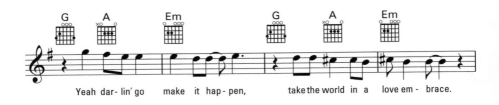

Yeah dar - lin' go make it hap - pen, take the world in a love em - brace.

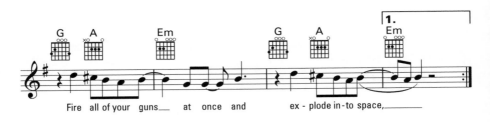

Fire all of your guns___ at once and ex - plode in-to space,___

1. Em

2, 3.

___ Like a true na - ture's child___ we were born, born to be wild___

we can climb so high_ I ne-ver want to die._____

Born to be wild,_____

Born to be wild._____

Instrumental solo

Play 6 times ad lib.

D.C.
Repeat instrumental to fade

Verse 2:
I like smoke and lightnin'
Heavy metal thunder
Racing with the wind
And the feeling that I'm under.

The Boys Are Back In Town

Words & Music by Phil Lynott

© Copyright 1976 Pippin The Friendly Ranger Music Company Limited.
Universal Music Publishing Limited.
All rights in Germany administered by Universal Music Publ. GmbH.
All Rights Reserved. International Copyright Secured.

Original key: A♭. To match original recording, use a capo, 1st fret.

Verse 2:
You know that chick that used to dance a lot?
Every night she'd be on the floor shakin' what she got
Man, when I tell you she was cool, she was red hot!
I mean she was steaming!
And that time over at Johnny's place
Well this chick got up and she slapped Johnny's face
Man, we fell about the place
If that chick don't want to know, forget her.

Verse 3:
Friday night, they'll be dressed to kill
Down at Dino's Bar and Grill
The drink will flow and the blood will spill
And if the boys wanna fight, you better let 'em
That juke-box in the corner blastin' out my favorite song
These nights are getting warmer
And it won't be long, won't be long till summer comes
Now that the boys are here again.

Cigarettes & Alcohol

Oasis' second UK top ten hit was, in spirit, a reprise of John Lennon's 'Working Class Hero', decrying dead-end jobs and recommending drug use as a legitimate response to bleak social prospects. The Lennon connection was reinforced with a flipside cover of 'I Am The Walrus' informally recorded at a 1994 Sony corporate event held at The Gleneagles Hotel in Perthshire, Scotland. Always susceptible to charges of ripping off their predecessors, Oasis were accused of plagiarising T-Rex's 'Get It On' for 'Cigarettes & Alcohol'. Even so the man who discovered the band, Alan McGee claimed that it was 'one of the greatest social statements' made in the past 25 years. The song's writer, Noel Gallagher, on the other hand merely thought that it 'keeps getting better and better for me'.

Oasis

Cigarettes & Alcohol

Words & Music by Noel Gallagher

© Copyright 1994 Creation Songs Limited/Oasis Music (GB).
Sony/ATV Music Publishing (UK) Limited.
All Rights Reserved. International Copyright Secured.

Verse 2:
Is it worth the aggravation to find yourself a job
When there's nothing worth working for?
It's a crazy situation, but all I need
Are cigarettes and alcohol.

47

Creep

Words & Music by Albert Hammond, Mike Hazlewood, Thom Yorke, Jonny Greenwood,
Colin Greenwood, Ed O'Brien & Phil Selway

© Copyright 1992 Warner/Chappell Music Limited (66.67%)/Imagem Songs Limited (33.33%).
All Rights Reserved. International Copyright Secured.

♩ = 92

1. When you were here be-fore,____ could-n't look you in the eye.____
(Verse 2 see block lyrics)

You're just like an an - gel, your skin makes me cry.____

You float like a fea - ther____ in a beau-ti-ful__ world.____
(Verse 4 see block lyrics)

I wish I was spe - cial, you're so fuck-ing spe - cial.____

But I'm a____ creep, I'm a____ weird - o.____

What the hell__ am I do-ing here?____ { I don't be-long____ here.____
{ I don't be-long____ here.____ Oh,

48

Verse 2:
I don't care if it hurts, I want to have control
I want a perfect body, I want a perfect soul
I want you to notice, when I'm not around
You're so fucking special, I wish I was special.

Verse 4:
Whatever makes you happy
Whatever you want
You're so fucking special
I wish I was special.

Cum On Feel The Noize

Words & Music by Jim Lea & Noddy Holder

© Copyright 1973 Barn Publishing (Slade) Limited.
All Rights Reserved. International Copyright Secured.

♩ = 136

1. So you think I've got an ev-il mind, well I'll tell___ you hon-ey,
(Verses 2 & 3 see block lyrics)
and I don't know___ why,___ and I don't know___ why.

So you think my sing-ing's out of time, well it makes___ me mon-ey,
and I don't know___ why,___ and I don't know why,

___ a-ny-more,_____ oh___ no.___ So cum on feel the noize,

and girls grab their boys,_____ we'll get wild, wild,___ wild,

50

Verse 2:
So you say I've got a funny face
Well that ain't no worry
And I don't know why
And I don't know why
Say I'm a scumbag but it's no disgrace
I ain't in no hurry
And I don't know why
And I just don't know why anymore, oh no.

Verse 3:
So you think we have a lazy time
Well, you should know better
And I don't know why
I just don't know why
And you say I've got a dirty mind
Well I'm a mean go-getter
And I don't know why
I just don't know why anymore, oh no.

51

Denis

Words & Music by Neil Levenson

© Copyright 1963 Neil Mel Music, USA.
Minder Music Limited.
All Rights Reserved. International Copyright Secured.

found   a   boy   like   you.___

3. De - nis, De - nis,   av - ec tes yeux si bleus;   De - nis, De - nis,
(Verse 4 see block lyrics)

moi j'ai flashe à nos deux: De - nis, De - nis,___   un grand bais - er d'é - ter - ni - té.

1.   **2.**

Oh, De - nis, oo be doo,   I'm in love with

you. De - nis, oo be doo,   I'm in love with you. De - nis, oo be

doo,   I'm   in   love with   you.___

Verse 2:
Oh, when we walk it always feels so nice
And when we talk, it seems like paradise
Denis, Denis I'm so in love with you.

Verse 4:
Denis, Denis je suis si folle de toi
Denis, Denis embrasse moi ce soir
Denis, Denis un grand baiser d'éternité.

A Design For Life

Words by Nicky Wire
Music by James Dean Bradfield, Nicky Wire & Sean Moore

© Copyright 1996 Sony/ATV Music Publishing (UK) Limited.
All Rights Reserved. International Copyright Secured.

54

(Don't Fear) The Reaper

Words & Music by Donald Roeser

© Copyright 1978 B O'Cult Songs Incoporated/Sony/ATV Tunes LLC, USA.
Sony/ATV Music Publishing (UK) Limited.
All Rights Reserved. International Copyright Secured.

57

Repeat ad lib. to fade

Verse 3:
Love of two is one
Here but now they're gone
Came the last night of sadness
And it was clear she couldn't go on
Then the door was open and the wind appeared
The candles blew and then disappeared
The curtains flew and then he appeared
(Saying don't be afraid.)

Come on baby
(And she had no fear)
And she ran to him
(Then they started to fly)
They looked backward and said goodbye
(She had become like they are)
She had taken his hand
(She had become like they are)
Come on baby
(Don't fear the Reaper.)

59

Don't You (Forget About Me)

Words & Music by Keith Forsey & Steve Schiff

© Copyright 1985 MCA Music (a division of MCA Incorporated), USA.
Universal/MCA Music Limited.
All rights in Germany administered by Universal/MCA Music Publ. GmbH.
All Rights Reserved. International Copyright Secured.

61

Verse 2:
Don't you try and pretend
It's my feeling we'll win in the end
I won't harm you
Or touch your defenses
Vanity, insecurity, uh-huh
Don't you forget about me
I'll be alone, dancing
You know, baby
Going to take you apart
I'll put us back together at heart baby.

Don't Stop

Fleetwood Mac's relentlessly feel-good 1977 song was, ironically, a response by Christine McVie to her separation from the band's bass player John McVie. 'Don't Stop' outlived the circumstances of its composition and has popped up over the years in a variety of settings when both optimism and a rolling rock song are called for. Notable examples were two Democratic party events where Bill Clinton first coaxed the disbanded group to play it at his inaugural ball in 1993, and then used their recording of the song at the 2000 Democratic convention after personally supplying a smooth if cheesy DJ-like link: 'Keep putting people first. Keep building those bridges. And don't stop thinking about tomorrow!'

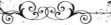

Don't Stop

Words & Music by Christine McVie

© Copyright 1976 Fleetwood Mac Music.
Universal Music Publishing MGB Limited.
All rights in Germany administered by Musik Edition Discoton GmbH (a division of Universal Music Publishing Group).
All Rights Reserved. International Copyright Secured.

Verse 2:
Why not think about times to come
And not about the things that you've done
If your life was bad to you
Just think what tomorrow will do.

Verse 3:
All I want is to see you smile
If it takes just a little while
I know you don't believe that it's true
I never meant any harm to you.

Eight Miles High

Words & Music by Gene Clark, Jim McGuinn & David Crosby

© Copyright 1966 Tickson Music Company, USA.
TRO Essex Music Limited.
All Rights Reserved. International Copyright Secured.

Verse 2:
Nowhere is there warmth to be found
Among those afraid of losing their ground
Rain grey town known for its sound
In places small faces unbound.

Verse 3:
Round the square huddled in storms
Some laughing some just shapeless forms
Sidewalk scenes and black limousines
Some living some standing alone.

Every Breath You Take

Words & Music by Sting

© Copyright 1983 Steerpike Limited/Steerpike (Overseas) Limited/EMI Music Publishing Limited.
All Rights Reserved. International Copyright Secured.

I look a-round but it's you I can't___ re - place;

I feel so cold and I long for your___ em - brace.

I keep cry - ing ba - by, ba - by please.___

D.S. al Coda

Oh, can't you___

Coda

ev - 'ry move___ you make, ev - 'ry step___ you take,

I'll be watch - ing you.

Repeat ad lib. to fade

I'll be watch - ing you.___

69

Eye Of The Tiger

Words & Music by Frank Sullivan III & Jim Peterik

© Copyright 1982 Rude Music Incorporated/Ensign Music Corporation/Famous Music Corporation (50%)/Warner/Chappell Music Limited (50%).
All Rights Reserved. International Copyright Secured.

Fix You

Words & Music by Guy Berryman, Chris Martin, Jon Buckland & Will Champion

© Copyright 2005 Universal Music Publishing MGB Limited.
All Rights in Germany Administered by Musik Edition Discoton GmbH (A Division of Universal Music Publishing Group).
All Rights Reserved. International Copyright Secured.

When you try____ your best but you don't suc-ceed,____ when you get____ what you want but not what you need,____ when you feel____ so tired but you can't sleep,____ stuck in re - verse.____ 2. And the tears____ come stream - ing down your face,____ *(Verse 3 see block lyrics)* when you lose____ some-thing you can't re- place,____ or you love____ some-one but it goes to waste,____ could it be worse?____

Lights will guide_____ you home_____ and ig -

- nite_____ your bones_____ and I will try_____ to fix you.

1.

3. And

2.

Guitar solo

Tears stream_ down your face when you lose some-thing

you can-not re - place. Tears stream_ down your face and

Lyrics under the staves:

I… Tears stream down your face.

I pro-mise you I will learn from my mis-takes. Tears stream

down your face and I…

Lights will guide you home and ig-

nite your bones and I will try to fix you.

Verse 3:
And high up above and down below
When you're too in love to let it go
But if you never try you'll never know
Just what you're worth.

Fool For Your Loving

Words & Music by David Coverdale, Bernie Marsden & Michael Moody

© Copyright 1980 EMI Music Publishing Limited (33.34%)/Warner/Chappell Music Limited (33.33%)/EMI Music Publishing (WP) Limited (33.33%).
All Rights Reserved. International Copyright Secured.

I was born un-der a bad___ sign,___ left out in the cold.

I'm a lone-ly man___ who knows___

___ just what it means___ to lose con - trol. But I took all the heart -
(Verse 2 see block lyrics)

- ache___ and turned it to shame,___ now I'm

mov - in', mov - in', on___ and I ain't tak - in' the blame.___

Don't come run - nin' to me, I know I've done___ all I

76

Verse 2:
I'm tired of hiding my feelings
You left me lonely too long
I gave you my heart and you tore it apart
Oh baby you done me wrong.

Fortunate Son

Words & Music by John Fogerty

© Copyright 1970 Jondora Music, USA.
Prestige Music Limited.
All Rights Reserved. International Copyright Secured.

1. Some folks are born, made to wave the flag, ooh, they're red, white and blue.
(Verses 2 & 3 see block lyrics)

And when the band plays "Hail to the chief", they point the can-non right at you.

It ain't me, it ain't me__ I ain't no sen-a-tor's son.

To Coda

It ain't me, it ain't me;__ I ain't no for-tun-ate one.

1. **2.** one.

1. **2. D.S. al Coda**

◆ Coda

Repeat ad lib. to fade

It ain't me, it ain't me;__ I ain't no for-tun-ate one.

Verse 2:
Some folks are born silver spoon in hand
Lord, don't they help themselves
But when the tax man comes to the door
Lord, the house looks like a rummage sale
It ain't me, it ain't me I ain't no millionaire's son.

Verse 3:
Some folks inherit star spangled eyes
Ooh, they send you down to war
And when you ask them, "How much should we give?"
They only answer "More! More! More!"
It ain't me, it ain't me I ain't no military son.

Free Bird

Words & Music by Allen Collins & Ronnie Van Zant

© Copyright 1973 Duchess Music Corporation, USA.
Universal/MCA Music Limited.
All rights in Germany administered by Universal/MCA Music Publ. GmbH.
All Rights Reserved. International Copyright Secured.

1. If I leave here to-mor - row, would you still re-mem-ber me? Well, I must be trav-el-ing on now, 'cause there's too ma-ny plac - es I've got to see. But if I stay here with you, girl, things just could-n't be the same. 'Cause I'm as free as a bird now, and this bird you can-not change, oh,

(Verse 2 see block lyrics)

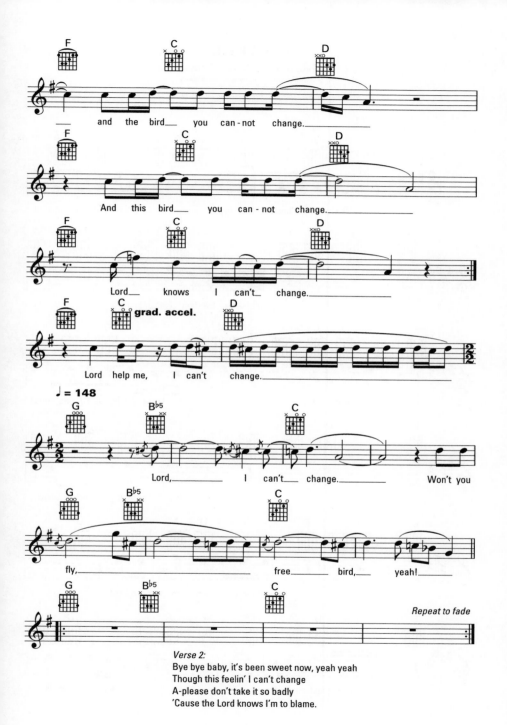

Verse 2:
Bye bye baby, it's been sweet now, yeah yeah
Though this feelin' I can't change
A-please don't take it so badly
'Cause the Lord knows I'm to blame.

Gloria

Words & Music by Van Morrison

© Copyright 1964 Hyde Park Music Publishing Limited.
Carlin Music Corporation.
All Rights Reserved. International Copyright Secured.

Like to tell you 'bout my ba-by, you know she comes a-

- round just be-fore five feet four____

from her head to the ground. You know she comes a-round here____

____ just a-bout mid-night,____

____ she makes me feel so good Lord,

she makes me feel all right.____ And her name is

Golden Touch

Words & Music by Johnny Borrell

© Copyright 2004 Sony/ATV Music Publishing (UK) Limited.
All Rights Reserved. International Copyright Secured.

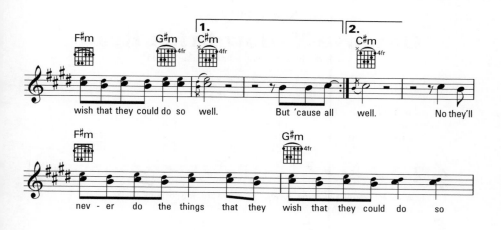

wish that they could do so well. But 'cause all well. No they'll

nev - er do the things that they wish that they could do so

well. They'll nev - er do the things that they

wish that they could do so_____ well. No they'll

nev - er do the things that they wish that they could do so_____ well.

Verse 2:
That kind of girl, yes she's never alone
You leave a thousand messages on her phone
But you know you'll never get through
And you could have it all if you wanted
You could have it all if it matters to you.

Goodbye Yellow Brick Road

Words & Music by Elton John & Bernie Taupin

© Copyright 1973 Dick James Music Limited.
Universal/Dick James Music Limited.
All rights in Germany administered by Universal Music Publ. GmbH.
All Rights Reserved. International Copyright Secured.

1. When are you gon-na come down, when are you going to land?_____ I

(Verse 2 see block lyrics)

should have stayed on the farm,_____ should have list - ened to my_ old man._____ You

know you can't hold_ me for-ev - er, I did-n't sign up_____ with you._

_____ I'm not a pre - sent for your friends to o - pen, this boy's too young to be

sing-ing_____ the blues._____ Ah.

Ah._____ So good-bye_____ yel-low brick road,_____ where the

88

Verse 2:
What do you think you'll do then?
I bet they shoot down your plane
It'll take you a couple of vodka and tonics
To get you on your feet again
Maybe you'll get a replacement
There's plenty like me to be found
Mongrels who ain't got a penny
Sniffing for titbits like you on the ground.

Grace

Words & Music by Jeff Buckley & Gary Lucas

© Copyright 1994 Sony/ATV Songs LLC, El Viejito Music & Gary Lucas Music, USA.
Sony/ATV Music Publishing (UK) Limited (50%)/Universal/MCA Music Limited (50%).
All rights in Germany administered by Universal/MCA Music Publ. GmbH.
All Rights Reserved. International Copyright Secured.

Tune bottom string to D

1. There's the moon ask-ing to stay long e-nough for the
(Verses 2 & 3 see block lyrics)
clouds to fly__ me a-way.__ Oh, it's my time com-ing,__
__ I'm__ not a-fraid,__ (a-) fraid__ to die.__

91

Verse 2:
And she weeps on my arm
Walking to the bright lights in sorrow
Oh, drink a bit of wine
We both might go tomorrow
Oh, my love
And the rain is falling
And I believe my time has come

It reminds me of the pain
I might leave, leave behind.

Verse 3:
And I feel them drown my name
So easy to know and forget with this kiss
I'm not afraid to go
But it goes so slow.

Hard To Handle

Words & Music by Otis Redding, Alvertis Isbell & Allen Jones

© Copyright 1968 Carlin Music Corporation.
All Rights Reserved. International Copyright Secured.

Original key: B. To match original recording, use a capo, 2nd fret.

1. Ba - by, here I am, I'm a man on the scene.

I can give you what you want but you got to go home with me.

I have got some good old lov - in' and I got some in store.

When I get through throw - in' it on you, you got to come back for more.

Boys and things that come by the doz - en, but that ain't noth - in' but drug store lov - in'.

93

Pret - ty lit - tle thing, let me light your can - dle 'cause

To Coda ⊕

D   E

Ma - ma I'm sure__ hard to han - dle now, yes, a - round.

G   D   A   A⁷

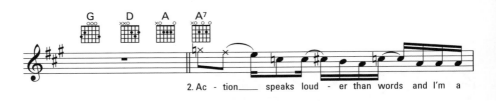

2. Ac - tion__ speaks loud - er than words and I'm a

man__ of great ex - per - i - ence. I__ know you've got you a - noth-er__ man, but I can

love you__ bet-ter than him.__ Take__ my hand don't be a - fraid, I'm gon-na

prove ev-'ry word I say.__ I'm__ ad - ver-tis - in' love__ for free_ so you can

place your ad__ with me.___ Boys that come a- long_ a dime by the doz- en,

that ain't noth - in' but ten cent lov- in'. Pret-ty lit-tle thing, let me light your can-dle 'cause

Ma - ma I'm sure__ hard to han-dle now, yes, a-round.

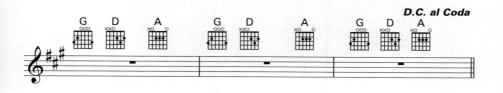

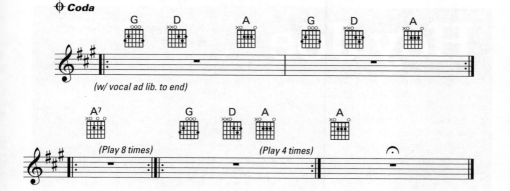

(w/ vocal ad lib. to end)

(Play 8 times)   (Play 4 times)

95

Hey Joe

For some years 'Hey Joe' was a song in waiting – a changeable number that sounded like a variation on a traditional theme but was also alleged to be an alternate take on everything from a Boudleaux Bryant country song to the informal product of a collaboration in the folk clubs of Edinburgh during the 1950s.

Then a group called The Leaves heard The Byrds perform it live, cut their own version and eventually, after a couple of re-recordings, became the only artists to have a US top 40 hit with it. Eventually its glory moment came when The Jimi Hendrix Experience released their version at the end of 1966. That became a big UK hit although it never even reached the charts in the US. Famously it was Hendrix's encore at Woodstock – the closing number of the entire festival – and went on to become a rock classic.

Hey Joe

Words & Music by Billy Roberts

© Copyright 1962 Third Story Music Company Incorporated, USA.
Carlin Music Corporation.
All Rights Reserved. International Copyright Secured.

Hey,___ Joe,___ uh where you go-in' with that gun in your hand?
(Verse 2 see block lyrics)

Hey,___ Joe, I said where you goin' with that gun

in your hand? Al - right. I'm go - in' down to shoot my old la - dy,

you know I caught her mess-in' 'round with an-oth - er man. Yeah.

I'm go - in' down to shoot my old la - dy, you know I caught her mess-in' 'round with an -

-oth - er man. Huh! And that ain't too cool.

Verse 2:
Uh, hey Joe, I heard you shot your woman down
You shot her down now
Uh, hey Joe, I heard you shot your old lady down
You shot her down in the ground, yeah
Yes, I did, I shot her
You know I caught her messin' 'round, messin' 'round town
Yes, I did, I shot her
You know I caught my old lady messin' 'round town
And I gave her the gun, I shot her!

Hush

Words & Music by Joe South

© Copyright 1967 Sony/ATV Songs LLC, USA.
Sony/ATV Music Publishing (UK) Limited.
All Rights Reserved. International Copyright Secured.

I got a south-ern lit - tle girl, she's on___ a my mind,

no doubt a-bout it, she looks so fine. The best girl that I ev - er had.___

What she do to make me feel so___ bad,___ yeah,

___ make me___ feel so___ bad. Hmm, yeah.

She got lov - in' like___ quick-sand, on - ly took___ one touch of my hand.

Blow-in' my mind, then I'm in so deep, can't a-eat, I___ can't

Ironic

Words by Alanis Morissette • Music by Alanis Morissette & Glen Ballard

© Copyright 1995 Music Corporation Of America Incorporated/Vanhurst Place Music/MCA Music Publishing/Aerostation Corporation, USA.
Universal/MCA Music Limited.
All rights in Germany administered by Universal/MCA Music Publ. GmbH.
All Rights Reserved. International Copyright Secured.

Original key: B. To match original recording, use a capo, 4th fret.

♩ = 85

An old man turned nine-ty eight, he won the lot-ter-y and
(Verse 2 see block lyrics)
died the next day. It's a black fly in your char-don-nay. It's a
death row par-don two min-utes too late. And is-n't it i - ron-ic? Don't ya
think? It's like rain on your wed-ding day. It's a free ride
when you've al-rea-dy paid. It's the good ad - vice
that you just did-n't take. And who would-'ve thought, it fi-gures?

To Coda

103

Verse 2:
Mr. Play-It-Safe was afraid to fly
He packed his suitcase and kissed his kids goodbye
He waited his whole damn life to take that flight
And as the plane crashed down he thought
"Well isn't this nice…"
And isn't it ironic… don't you think.

I Predict A Riot

Words & Music by Nicholas Hodgson, Richard Wilson, Andrew White, James Rix & Nicholas Baines

© Copyright 2004 Imagem Music Limited.
All Rights Reserved. International Copyright Secured.

♩ = 160

1. Oh, watch-ing the peo - ple get lai - ry is
(Verse 2 see block lyrics)

not ve - ry pret - ty, I tell thee. Walk-ing through town is quite

sca - ry, and not ve-ry sen - si-ble ei - ther. A friend of a friend, he got

beat - en, he looked the wrong way at a po - lice - man; would

ne - ver have hap - pened to Smea - ton, an old Le - o - den - si - an.

La, la, la, la, la, la, la. Ah,

Verse 2:
Oh, I try to get to my taxi
A man in a tracksuit attacks me
He said that he saw it before me
Wants to get things a bit gory
Girls run around with no clothes on
To borrow a pound for a condom
If it wasn't for chip fat they'd be frozen
They're not very sensible.

107

I Want You (She's So Heavy)

Words & Music by John Lennon & Paul McCartney

© Copyright 1969 Sony/ATV Music Publishing (UK) Limited.
All Rights Reserved. International Copyright Secured.

It's A Long Way To The Top
(If You Wanna Rock 'n' Roll)

Words & Music by Angus Young, Malcolm Young & Bon Scott

© Copyright 1975 J. Albert & Son Pty. Limited.
All Rights Reserved. International Copyright Secured.

1. Rid-in' down the high-way, go-in' to a show stop
get-tin' stoned, get-tin' beat up, bro-ken boned. Get-tin' had,

(Verse 2 see block lyrics)

___ in' all the by-ways, play-in' rock 'n' roll. Get-tin' robbed,
Get-tin' took, I tell you folks, it's harder than it looks. It's a

long way to the top___ if you wan-na rock 'n' roll.___ {It's a
{If you

think it's ea-sy do-in' one-night stands, try play-in' in a rock 'n' roll band. } It's a
wan-na be a star of stage and screen, look out, it's tough and mean. }

D.C. 3 times
2° Bagpipe solo

long way to the top___ if you wan-na rock 'n' roll___ It's a long way to the top

(Play 3 times) *Repeat to fade*

___ if you wan-na rock 'n' roll.___ It's a long way. It's a

Verse 2:
It's a hotel motel make you wanna cry
Ladies do the hard sell, know the reason why
Gettin' old, gettin' grey

Gettin' ripped off, underpaid
Gettin' sold, second hand
That's how it goes, playing in a band.

110

Jack And Diane

Words & Music by John Cougar Mellencamp

© Copyright 1982 Riva Music Limited.
EMI Music Publishing (WP) Limited.
All Rights Reserved. International Copyright Secured.

1. Lit - tle dit - ty 'bout Jack and Di - ane, _____

(Verses 2 & 3 see block lyrics)

two 'mer - i - can kids grow - in' up in the heart - land. Jack - ie gon' be a

foot - ball star, _____ Di - ane's deb - u - tante back seat of Jack - ie's car. _____

1.

(Guitar)

2.3.

Oh, yeah _____ life goes on, _____

long af - ter the thrill of liv - in' is _____ gone. Oh, yeah _____ life

life goes on,___ long af - ter the thrill of liv - in' is___ gone.___

Oh, yeah, I say life___ goes on,___ long af - ter the thrill of

liv-ing is___ gone. A lit-tle dit-ty 'bout Jack and Di - ane,___

two 'mer - i-can kids_ do - in' best that they_ can.

N.C.

Repeat to fade

(Guitar)

Verse 2:
Sucking on a chilli dog outside the Tastee Freeze
Diane sitting on Jackie's lap, he's got his hands between her knees
Jackie say: "Hey Diane, let's run off behind a shady tree,
Dribble off those Bobby Brooks let me do what I please."

Verse 3:
Jackie sits back, collects his thoughts for the moment,
Scratches his head and does his best James Dean
"Well, hey there Diane, we ought-a run off to the city."
Diane says: "Baby, you ain't missing nothing." And Jackie say:

113

Jeremy

Words by Eddie Vedder • Music by Jeff Ament

© Copyright 1991 Innocent Bystander/Scribing C-Ment Songs, USA.
Universal Music Publishing Limited (50%)/Sony/ATV Music Publishing (UK) Limited (50%).
All rights in Germany administered by Universal Music Publ. GmbH.
All Rights Reserved. International Copyright Secured.

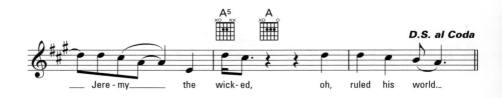

_Jere - my____ the wick- ed, oh, ruled his world.__

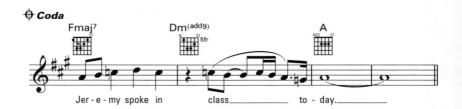

Jer - e - my spoke in class____ to - day.____

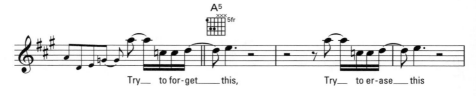

Try__ to for-get____ this, Try__ to er-ase__ this

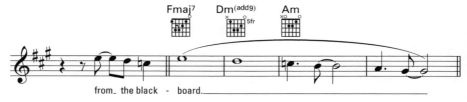

from_ the black - board.____

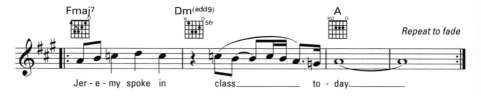

Jer - e - my spoke in class____ to - day.____

116

Jailhouse Rock

If the collected films of Elvis Presley are little more than a serial display of opportunism and bad taste, there were one or two exceptions. Perhaps *Jailhouse Rock* (1957) was not the finest, but it was among the best, being rooted in some sort of reality. Jerry Leiber and Mike Stoller provided the title song, and it turned out to be a great rock 'n' roll number packed with energy and wit. As performed in the film (on a stylised prison set) it teeters on the edge of being the traditional Hollywood musical number (let's do the show right here!) but as an Elvis movie song it did offer the early promise of a halfway decent movie career that wouldn't shame The King's rock credentials. That promise was not kept but 'Jailhouse Rock' was at least a thrilling taste of what might have been.

Jailhouse Rock

Words & Music by Jerry Leiber & Mike Stoller

© Copyright 1957 Elvis Presley Music, USA.
Carlin Music Corporation.
All Rights Reserved. International Copyright Secured.

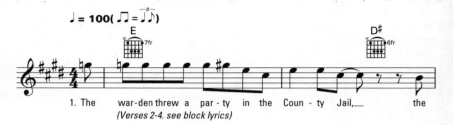

1. The war-den threw a par-ty in the Coun-ty Jail,___ the
(Verses 2-4. see block lyrics)

pri-son band was there they be-gan to wail,___ the

band was jump-in' and the joint be-gan to swing, you should have heard those knocked out

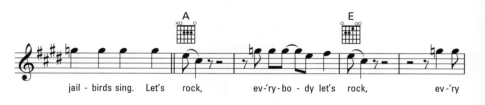

jail-birds sing. Let's rock, ev'ry-bo-dy let's rock, ev'ry

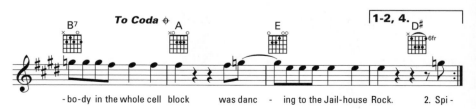

-bo-dy in the whole cell block was danc - ing to the Jail-house Rock. 2. Spi-

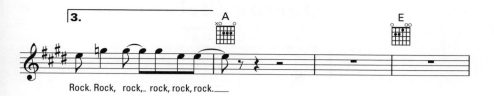

Rock. Rock, rock, rock, rock, rock.___

D.S. al Coda
with repeats

4. The

Coda

block   was danc - ing to the Jail-house Rock.   Danc -

- ing   to   the   Jail - house   Rock.   Danc -

Report to fade

- ing   to   the   Jail - house   Rock.   Danc -

Verse 2:
Spider Murphy played the tenor saxophone
Little Joe was blowin' on the slide trombone
The drummer boy from Illinois went crash, boom, bang
The whole rhythm section was a purple gang.

Verse 3:
Number forty-seven said to number three:
"You're the cutest jailbird I ever did see.
I sure would be delighted with your company,
Come on and do the jailhouse rock with me."

Verse 4:
Sad sack was a sittin' on a block of stone
Way over in the corner weepin' all alone
The warden said; "Hey, buddy, don't you be no square,
If you can't find a partner use a wooden chair."

Verse 5:
Shifty Henry said to Bugs: "For heavens sake,
No ones lookin', nows our chance to make a break."
Bugsy turned to Shifty and he said: "Nix nix,
I wanna stick around a while and get my kicks."

Jersey Girl

Words & Music by Tom Waits

© Copyright 1980 Fifth Floor Music Incorporated, USA.
All Rights Reserved. International Copyright Secured.

120

when I'm walk-in' down the street   with__ you. Sing sha la la   la la la,____

sha la la la la la   la__ la la.__   Sha la la   la la la la la.

Sha la la, well,_ I'm in love with a Jer - sey girl._____   Sha   la la la la.__

Sha la la la la la la   la__ la la.__   Sha la la   la la la la la.

Sha la la   la la la.   2. You   know she thrills me with
                                        3. I see you on the street and you

(Sax solo)

Verse 2:
You know she thrills me with all her charms
When I'm wrapped up in my baby's arms
My little girl gives me everything
I know some day that she'll wear my ring
So don't bother me, man, I got no time
I'm on my way to see that girl of mine
'Cause nothin' matters in this whole wide world
When you're in love with a Jersey girl.

Verse 3:
I see you on the street and you look so tired
Girl, I know that job you got leaves you so uninspired
When I come back to take you out to eat
You're lyin' all dressed up on the bed, baby, fast asleep
Go in the bathroom put your makeup on
We're gonna take that little brat of yours
And drop her off at your mom's
I know a place where the dancing's free
Now baby won't you come with me.

121

Johnny B. Goode

Words & Music by Chuck Berry

© Copyright 1958 Arc Music Corporation, USA.
Jewel Music Publishing Company Limited.
All Rights Reserved. International Copyright Secured.

♩ = 168

1. Deep down in Lou -'si - an - a close to New Or - leans,_ way

(Verses 2 & 3 see block lyrics)

back up in the woods a - mong the ev - er - greens,_ there

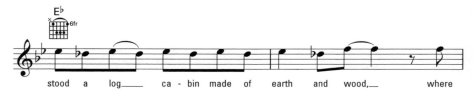

stood a log___ ca - bin made of earth and wood,_ where

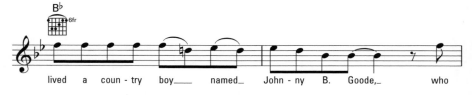

lived a coun - try boy___ named_ John - ny B. Goode,_ who

nev - er ev - er learned to read or write so well,_ but he could

play a gui - tar___ just like a ring - in' a bell. Go! Go!

Verse 2:
He used to carry his guitar in a gunny sack
Go sit beneath the tree by the railroad track
Ol' engineers would see him sittin' in the shade
Strummin' with the rhythm that the drivers made
The people passin' by, they would stop and say
"Oh my, but that little country boy could play."

Verse 3:
His mother told him, "Someday you will be a man,
And you will be the leader of a big ol' band.
Many people comin' from miles around,
Will hear you play your music when the sun goes down.
Maybe someday your name will be in lights,
Sayin' 'Johnny B. Goode Tonight'." Go! Go!

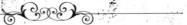

The Joker

Words & Music by Steve Miller, Eddie Curtis & Ahmet Ertegun

© Copyright 1974 Sailor Music/Jim Rooster Music/Warner-Tamerlaine Music, USA.
P & P Songs Limited.
All Rights Reserved. International Copyright Secured.

124

pick-er, I'm a grin-ner, I'm a lov-er, and I'm a sin-ner.

I play my mu-sic in the sun.___ I'm a

jok-er, I'm a smok-er, I'm a mid-night___ tok-er.

1, 3.

{ I get my lov-ing on___ the run. Ooh.___
{ I sure don't want to hurt no-

2.

3° **D.C.** *(to fade)*

D.S.

___ Ooh.___ - one.___

Verse 2:
(Instrumental)
You're the cutest thing that I ever did see
Love your peaches, want to shake your tree
Lovey dovey, lovey dovey, lovey dovey all the time
Ooh-wee, baby, I should show you a good time.

Verse 3:
People keep talking about me baby
Say I'm doin' you wrong
But don't you worry, don't you worry
No, don't worry Mama, 'cause I'm right at home
You're the cutest thing that I ever did see
Love your peaches, want to shake your tree
Lovey dovey, lovey dovey, lovey dovey all the time
Ooh-wee, baby, I should show you a good time.

Knockin' On Heaven's Door

Words & Music by Bob Dylan

© Copyright 1973 Ram's Horn Music, USA.
All Rights Reserved. International Copyright Secured.

To match original recording, tune down one semitone.

Verse 2:
Mama, put my guns in the ground
I can't shoot them anymore
That black cloud is comin' down
Feels like I'm knockin' on Heaven's door.

The Logical Song

Words & Music by Roger Hodgson & Richard Davies

© Copyright 1979 Almo Music Corporation, USA/Delicate Music, USA.
Rondor Music (London) Limited.
All rights in Germany administered by Rondor Musikverlag GmbH.
All Rights Reserved. International Copyright Secured.

1. When I was young,— it seemed that life was so won-der-ful.
(Verses 2 & 3 see block lyrics)

a mir-a-cle, oh, it was beau-ti-ful, mag-i-cal. And all the

birds in the trees,— well they'd be sing-ing so hap-pi-ly,

oh, joy-ful-ly, oh, play-ful-ly

1, 3. / **2, 4.**

watch-ing me. | 2. But then they | *1°* There are times—
2° At night,—

127

when all___ the world's a-sleep,___ the ques-

-tions run___ too deep___ for such___ a sim-ple man.___

Won't you please,___ please

tell me what___ we've learned?___ I know___ it sounds___ ab-surd___

2° To Coda ⊕

___ please tell me who___ I am.___

D.S. al Coda

___ I said

128

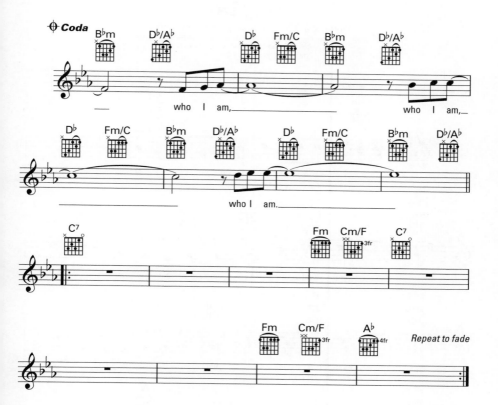

Verse 2:
But they sent me away to teach me how to be sensible
Logical, oh, responsible, practical
And they showed me a world where I could be so dependable
Oh, clinical oh, intellectual, cynical.

Verse 3:
I said, watch what you say or they'll be calling you a radical
A liberal, oh, fanatical, criminal
Oh, won't you sign up your name, we'd like to feel you're acceptable
Respectable, oh, presentable. A vegetable!

Layla

Words & Music by Eric Clapton & Jim Gordon

© Copyright 1970, 1998 & 2004 Warner/Chappell Music Limited.
All Rights Reserved. International Copyright Secured.

Verse 2:
Tried to give you consolation
Your old man had let you down
Like a fool, I fell in love with you
You turned my whole world upside down.

Verse 3:
Make the best of the situation
Before I finally go insane
Please don't say we'll never find a way
Tell me all my love's in vain.

Live And Let Die

Words & Music by Paul & Linda McCartney

© Copyright 1973 MPL Communications Limited (75%)/EMI United Partnership Limited (25%).
All Rights Reserved. International Copyright Secured.

♩ = 66

When you were young and your heart was an o-pen book,_

*2° Instrumental till ***

you used to say live and let live. (You know you did, you know you did, you know you

did.)_ But if this ev-er-chang-ing world in which we live in makes you

give in and cry,_ say live and let die!_

Live and let die,_ live and let

die,_ live and let die._

What does it mat - ter to ya, when you got a job to do __ you got - ta

do it well, __ you got - ta give the oth - er fel - low hell! __

Livin' On A Prayer

New Jersey is the only American state that doesn't have an official anthem, but 'Livin' On A Prayer' could be the people's choice...or perhaps their second choice after more or less anything by Bruce Springsteen. Jersey native John Francis Bongiovi Jr. wrote his song-story about a working class couple battling the bad times and then he recorded it twice, dissatisfied with the first version.

The song proved highly versatile, later being pressed into inspirational service for everything from The Boston Red Sox, John Kerry's presidential campaign and two 9/11 concerts. Bon Jovi reworked it in acoustic versions as well and also referenced its lyrics in several later songs. How the band felt about the cover version by Alvin and The Chipmunks is not recorded.

Bon Jovi

Livin' On A Prayer

Words & Music by Jon Bon Jovi, Richie Sambora & Desmond Child

© Copyright 1986 Bon Jovi Publishing/PolyGram International Music Publishing Incorporated/Aggressive Music/Sony/ATV Tunes LLC, USA.
Universal Music Publishing Limited (66.67%) (administered in Germany by Universal Music Publ. GmbH)/
Sony/ATV Music Publishing (UK) Limited (33.33%).
All Rights Reserved. International Copyright Secured.

1. Tom-my used to work on the docks,_____ u-nion's been on strike. He's
(Verse 2 see block lyrics)
down on his luck, it's tough,____ so tough.____ Gi-na works the di-ner all day,__
____ work-ing for her man. She brings home her pay for love,____
nn,____ for love.____ She says, "We've got-ta hold__ on__ to
what we've got, it does-n't make a diffe-rence if we make it or not, we've got each oth-er and
that's a lot. For__ love____ we'll give it a shot. Oh,_____ we're half-way there,

oh, oh,___ liv - in' on a pray-er. Take my hand, we'll make it I swear, oh, oh,___ liv-

1. D **Em** **2.**

- in' on a pray-er."   - in' on a pray-er. Liv-in' on___ a prayer.___

Em Cadd9 D G D

Em Cadd9 D G Em

Ooh,_____ we've got to

C D Em D C D

hold_ on,___ rea-dy or_ not. You live for the fight when that's all that's you've got.

Gm Ebadd9 F Bb Eb F

Repeat to fade

{ Oh,_____ we're half-way there.__ } Oh, oh,___ liv - in' on a pray-er.
{ Take my hand and we'll make it I swear__ }

Verse 2:
Tommy's got his six-string in hock
Now he's holding in
When he used to make it talk so tough
Mm, it's tough

Gina dreams of running away
When she cries in the night
Tommy whispers
"Baby it's okay, someday."

London Calling

Words & Music by Joe Strummer, Mick Jones, Paul Simonon & Topper Headon

© Copyright 1979 Nineden Limited/Universal Music Publishing Limited.
All rights in Germany administered by Universal Music Publ. GmbH.
All Rights Reserved. International Copyright Secured.

1. Lon-don call - ing to the far-a-way towns, now war is de - clared and
(Verse 2 see block lyrics)

bat - tle come down, Lon-don call-ing to the und - er - world, come out of the cup - board, you

boys and girls.__ Lon-don call - ing now don't look to us, phon-ey Beat-le- man - ia has

bit-ten the dust. Lon-don call-ing see we ain't got no swing ex - cept for the ring__ of that

trunch-eon thing. The ice age is com-ing, the sun's zoom-ing in,__ melt-down__ ex-pec-ted, the

wheat is__ grow-ing thin. En-gines stop run-ning, but I have no fear 'cause

Verse 2:
London calling, to the imitation zone
Forget it brother you can go it alone
London calling, to the zombies of death
Quit holding out and draw another breath
London calling, and I don't want to shout
But while we were talking I saw you nodding out

London calling, see we ain't got no high
Except for that one with the yellowy eyes.

Bridge 2:
The ice age is coming, the sun's zooming in
Engines stop running, the wheat is growing thin
A nuclear error, but I have no fear
'Cause London is drowning, and I, I live by the river.

Louie Louie

Words & Music by Richard Berry

© Copyright 1957 Windswept Pacific Entertainment Company d/b/a Longitude Music Company, USA.
EMI Music Publishing (WP) Limited.
All Rights Reserved. International Copyright Secured.

140

sailed that___ ship___ ah all a - lone.___ Me

1, 2.
nev - er think how___ I'll make it home.___ Uh

3.
tell her___ I'll___ nev - er leave her here.___ Uh

D.S. al Coda

Coda
we got-ta go. I said we got-ta go now.

Spoken: Take this one outta here. *Shouted:* Let's go!

Verse 2:
Three nights and days I sailed the sea
Me think of girl oh constantly
Oh, on that ship I dream she there
I smell the rose, in her hair.

Verse 3:
Me see Jamaica ah moon above
It won't be long me see me love
Me take her in my arms again
I tell her I'll never leave her here.

Love Bites

Words & Music by Joe Elliott, Rick Savage, Steve Clark, Phil Collen & Robert John 'Mutt' Lange

© Copyright 1986 Bludgeon Riffola Limited/Sony/ATV Music Publishing Limited (80%)/Out Of Pocket Productions Limited/Imagem London Limited (20%).
All Rights Reserved. International Copyright Secured.

142

'cause mak-ing love to you___ might drive___ me cra - zy._____ 2° (Love

1° & 3° only

I know you think that love___ is the way you make___ it,_____

so I don't wan-na be there___ when you de-cide to break___ it. No! (Love

bites,   love bleeds.)   It's bring-ing me to___ my knees.___ (Love

lives,   love dies.)   It's not a sur - prise.___ (Love___

begs,   love pleads.)   It's what I need.   It's what I need.

143

Love Is The Drug

Words & Music by Bryan Ferry & Andy Mackay

© Copyright 1975 EG Music Limited.
Universal Music Publishing MGB Limited.
All Rights in Germany Administered by Musik Edition Discoton GmbH (A Division of Universal Music Publishing Group).
All Rights Reserved. International Copyright Secured.

♩ = 124

Dm — T'ain't no big thing to wait for the bell to ring, t'ain't

Dm **C** **Am** — no__ big thing, the toll of the bell.

Dm **F** **Am** — Ag-gra-va-ted spare for days, I troll down-town, the red light place. I

Dm **C** **Am** — jump up bub-ble up, what's in store? Love is the drug and I need_ to score.

Dm **F** **Am** — Show-ing out, show-ing out, hit and run, boy meets girl where the beat goes on.

Em **G** **Am** — Stitched up tight, can't shake_ free, love is the drug_ got a hook on me.

Oh_____ catch that buzz, love is the drug I'm think-ing of.

Oh_____ can't you see_ love is the drug for me?

Oh,_____

Late that night I parked my car,_ stake my place in the sin-gles bar._

Face to face, toe to toe, heart to heart as we hit the floor.

Lum-ber_ up, lim-bo down, the locked em-brace, the stum-ble 'round.

I say "go" she say_"yes" dim the lights, you can guess the rest.

146

Oh___ {catch / get} that buzz, love is the drug I'm think-ing of. Oh___

can't you see_ {love is the drug got a / love, the drug_ for} {hook in me? / me.} Oh,_____

oh,_____ oh,_____ oh,_____

oh,_____ oh,_____

oh,_____ oh,_____ oh,_____

oh,_____

Love is, love is, love is___ the drug.

Lust For Life

The title track from Iggy Pop's 1977 album was as challenging as you might expect from a song co-written by Iggy and David Bowie. Including characters from an experimental novel by William S. Burroughs and, according to a member of The Doors, also immortalising their deceased real-life drug dealer Gypsy Johnny, 'Lust For Life' was more a frenetic celebration of excess than any decipherable narrative. It acquired extra notoriety when Iggy Pop sang it on TV in The Netherlands, destroying an inexpensive studio set in the process, apparently by previous arrangement with the TV company. Latterly Iggy's lust for life has been profitably recycled to promote an insurance company (slogan: 'Get A Life!') but back in the 1970s, his wild-child antics never found a better song than this one, even if it did borrow a riff – as well as a character – from The Doors.

Lust For Life

Words & Music by David Bowie & Iggy Pop

© Copyright 1977 Tintoretto Music/RZO Music Limited (42%)/EMI Music Publishing Limited (14.25%)/James Osterberg Music/EMI Virgin Music Limited (43.75%).
All Rights Reserved. International Copyright Secured.

1. *Tacet vocal*
2. Here comes John-ny in____ a-gain____ with the liq-uor and drugs
(*Verses 3 & 4 see block lyrics*)

(2.) and a fast ma-chine. He's gon-na do an-oth-er strip-tease.

Hey man, where'd you get____ that lo - tion? I've been

hurt-ing since I'm up a - gain____ a-bout some-thing called love, yeah,

some-thing called love. Well that's like hyp-no-tiz - ing chick-ens.

Well, I'm just____ a mo-dern guy;____ of course I've had it in____ my

(Ooh.)_____ I got a lust for life.

Well, I'm just_____ a mo-dern guy;_____ of course I've

had it in_____ my ear be-fore,_____ 'cause I've a lust for life,

'cause I've a lust for life.

4. Well,

Verse 3:
I'm worth a million in prizes
With my torture film
Drive a G.T.O., uniform
All on a government loan
I'm worth a million in prizes
Yeah, I'm through with sleeping
On the sidewalk, beating my brains
With liquor and drugs
With liquor and drugs.

Verse 4:
Here comes Johnny in again
With the liquor and drugs
And a fast machine
He's gonna do another striptease
Hey man, where'd you get that lotion?
Your skin starts itchin'
Once you buy the gimmick
About something called love
Oh love, love, love
Well that's like hypnotizing chickens.

Mind Games

Words & Music by John Lennon

© Copyright 1973 Lenono Music.
All Rights Reserved. International Copyright Secured.

♩ = 70

We're play-ing these mind games to - geth - er,___ push-ing the bar - ri-ers,___ plant-ing seeds.___ Play-ing the mi - nd___ guer - li-la, chant-ing the man - tra "peace on earth."___ We all been play-ing those mind games for - ev - er,___ some kind-a dru - id dudes lift-ing the veil.___ Do-ing the mi - nd___ guer - il - la, some call it ma - gic, the search for the grail.

1. Love is the ans-wer_ and you know that for sure.
(Verse 3 see block lyrics)

Love____ is a flow-er,____ you got-ta let it, you got-ta let it

grow. So keep on play-ing those mind games to - geth-er,____ faith in the fu -

- ture, out of the now.____ You just can't beat on those

mi - nd__ guer - ril - las, ab-so-lute else -

- where in the stones of your mind. Yeah, we're play-ing those mind games for -

153

Verse 2:
Yes is the answer and you know that for sure
Yes is surrender you gotta let it, you gotta let it go
So keep on playing those mind games together
Doing the ritual, dance in the sun
Millions of mind guerrillas
Putting their soul power to the karmic wheel
Keep on playing those mind games forever
Raising the spirit of peace and love.

More Than A Feeling

Words & Music by Tom Scholz

© Copyright 1976 Pure Songs, USA.
Sony/ATV Music Publishing (UK) Limited.
All Rights Reserved. International Copyright Secured.

1. I looked out this mor-ning and the sun was gone, turned on some mu - sic to
(Verse 2 see block lyrics)

start my____ day.__ I lost my-self____ in a fa-mil - iar song, I closed my____ eyes_ and I

slipped a - way._____ *(Guitar)*

It's more than a feel - ing, when I hear that old song____ they used to play.__ It's

I be-gin dream - ing, when I see Mar-i - anne____ walk a - way.

I see my Mar - i-anne walk-ing a - way.

(Bass)

(Guitar solo)

(Bass)

3. When I'm tired___ and think - ing cold

hide in my mu - sic, for - get the__ day,__ and dream of a girl___ I used to know.

closed my_____ eyes_ and she slipped a - way._____

She slipped a - way_____

It's

more than a feel - ing,   when I   hear that old song_____ they used to play._____

I be - gin dream - ing,   when I   see Mar - i - anne_____ walk a - way.

Repeat to fade

Verse 2:
So many people have come and gone
Their faces fade as the years go by
Yet I still recall as I wander on
As clear as the sun in the summer sky.

My Sharona

Words & Music by Douglas Fieger & Berton Averre

© Copyright 1979 Small Hill Music/Eighties Music/Wise Brothers Music LLC, USA.
Universal Music Publishing MGB Limited (75%) (administered in Germany by Musik Edition Discoton GmbH, a division of Universal Music Publishing Group)/
Campbell Connelly & Company Limited (25%).
All Rights Reserved. International Copyright Secured.

1. Oh_____ my lit-tle pret-ty one,
3. When_____ *(Verses 2 & 3 see block lyrics)*

my pret-ty one, when_____ you gon-na give me some time, Sha-ro-na? Ooh,__

_____you make my mo-tor run, my mo-tor run, gun___ it com-ing off of the

line, Sha-ro-na. Ne - ver gon-na stop, give it up, such a dir-ty mind, I

al-ways get it up for the touch of the young-er kind. My, my,___ my -

To Coda

- y - y wow! M-m-m-my Sha-ro-na.

1.

2. Come

158

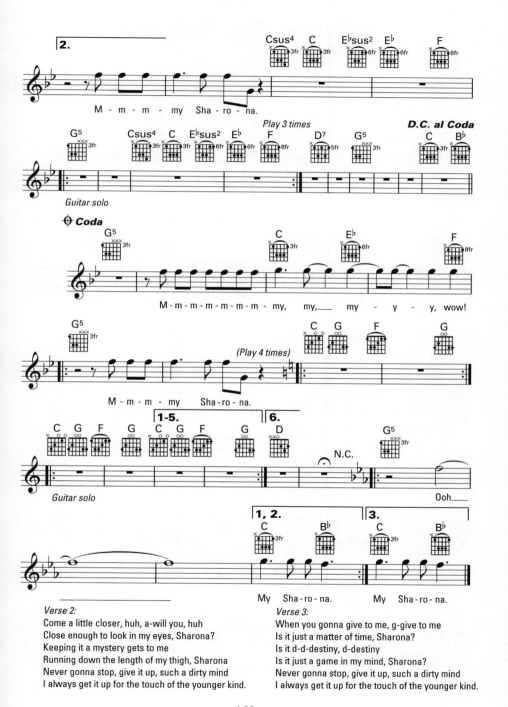

Verse 2:
Come a little closer, huh, a-will you, huh
Close enough to look in my eyes, Sharona?
Keeping it a mystery gets to me
Running down the length of my thigh, Sharona
Never gonna stop, give it up, such a dirty mind
I always get it up for the touch of the younger kind.

Verse 3:
When you gonna give to me, g-give to me
Is it just a matter of time, Sharona?
Is it d-d-destiny, d-destiny
Is it just a game in my mind, Sharona?
Never gonna stop, give it up, such a dirty mind
I always get it up for the touch of the younger kind.

Nothing Else Matters

Words & Music by James Hetfield & Lars Ulrich

© Copyright 1991 Creeping Death Music, USA.
Universal Music Publishing Limited.
All rights in Germany administered by Universal Music Publ. GmbH.
All Rights Reserved. International Copyright Secured.

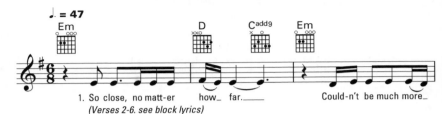

1. So close, no matt-er how_ far._
(Verses 2-6. see block lyrics)
Could-n't be much more_

from the heart.___ For-ev-er trust-ing who we are.___

1, 2, 4, 5. And no-thing else mat-ters.___ **3, 6.** mat-ters.___

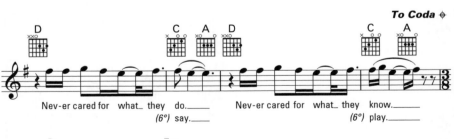

To Coda

Nev-er cared for what_ they do.___ Nev-er cared for what_ they know.___
(6°) say._ *(6°) play._*

D.S. al Coda

Oh, but I know.___

160

Coda

Nev-er cared for what they do. Nev-er cared for what they know. Oh, and I know. Yeah, yeah.

(Instrumental) So close, no mat-ter how far, could-n't be much more from the heart. For ev-er trust-ing who we are.

No no-thing else mat-ters.

Repeat to fade

Verse 2:
Never opened myself this way
Life is ours we live it our way
All these words I don't just say
And nothing else matters.

Verse 3:
Trust I seek and I find in you
Everyday for us something new
Open mind for a different view
And nothing else matters.

Verse 4:
So close, no matter how far
Couldn't be much more from the heart
All these words I don't just say
And nothing else matters.

Verse 5:
Never opened myself this way
Life is ours we live it our way
All these words I don't just say
And nothing else matters.

Verse 6:
Trust I seek and I find in you
Everyday for us something new
Open mind for a different view
And nothing else matters.

161

No Woman, No Cry

Words & Music by Vincent Ford

© Copyright 1974 Fifty-Six Hope Road Music Limited/Odnil Music Limited.
Blue Mountain Music Limited.
All Rights Reserved. International Copyright Secured.

162

good friends we've lost__ a-long the way.__

In__ this bright fu - ture you__ can't for - get your_ past

so, dry your tears I__ say. And Ev-'ry-thing's gon-na be all right.

Ev -'ry-thing's gon-na be all right. Ev -'ry-thing's gon-na be all right.

1. Ev-'ry-thing's gon-na be all right. **2.** Ev-'ry-thing's gon-na be all right so, wo-man, no cry.

No, no wo-man, no wo-man, no cry.__

Oh, my lit-tle sis-ter don't shed no tears. No wo-man, no cry.__

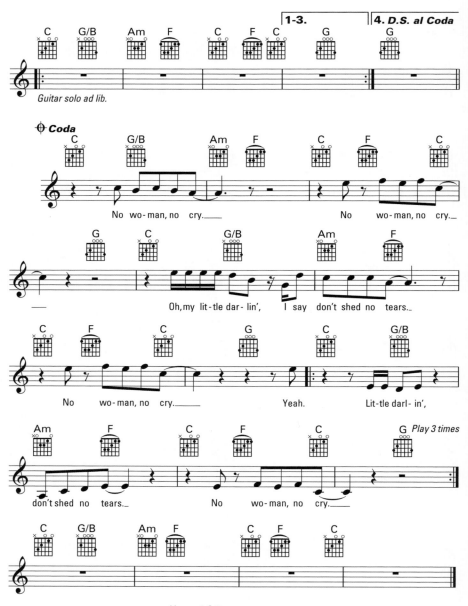

Verses 2 & 3:
And then Georgie would make a fire light
As it was log wood burnin' through the night
Then we would cook corn meal porridge
Of which I'll share with you
My feet is my only carriage
So, I've got to push on through
But while I'm gone I mean...

Oliver's Army

Words & Music by Elvis Costello

© Copyright 1978 Universal Music Publishing MGB Limited.
All rights in Germany administered by Musik Edition Discoton GmbH (a division of Universal Music Publishing Group).
All Rights Reserved. International Copyright Secured.

1. Don't start me talk - ing; I could talk all night.

(Verse 2 see block lyrics)

My mind goes sleep-walk-ing while I'm put-ting the world to right.

Called car - eers in - for-ma - tion. Have you got your-self an oc - cu-pa-

Ol - i-ver's ar - my is here to stay. Ol - i-ver's ar - my are on their way.
- tion?

And I would rath-er be an - y-where else but here to -

1.
2.

- day.

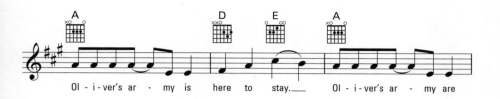

Ol - i - ver's ar - my is here to stay.___ Ol - i - ver's ar - my are

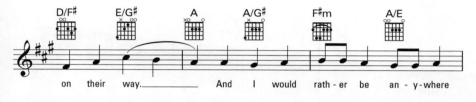

on their way._____ And I would rath - er be an - y - where

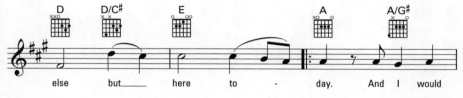

else but___ here to - day. And I would

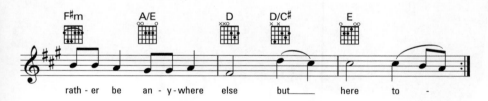

rath - er be an - y - where else but___ here to -

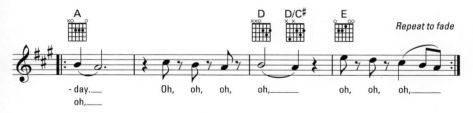

- day.___ Oh, oh, oh, oh,___ oh, oh, oh,___
oh,___

Verse 2:
There was a checkpoint Charlie
He didn't crack a smile
But it's no laughing party when you've been on the Murder Mile
Only takes one itchy trigger
One more widow, one less white nigger.

Paranoid

Legend has it that back in 1970 Black Sabbath guitarist Tony Iommi came up with the riff for 'Paranoid' while the rest of the band was out to lunch. Vocalist Ozzie Osbourne would soon show signs of remaining that way indefinitely, but when they reassembled on the day in question, the band recorded the song almost immediately with Osbourne making up lyrics as he went along. Later the band's bassist and lyricist Geezer Butler wrote new ones. The song would become almost a signature tune for Black Sabbath and has since lent itself to a variety of movie soundtracks, TV programmes and video games.

Black Sabbath

Paranoid

Words & Music by Ozzy Osbourne, Tony Iommi, Terry 'Geezer' Butler & Bill Ward

© Copyright 1970 Westminster Music Limited.
All Rights Reserved. International Copyright Secured.

1. Fin-ished with_ my wo - man 'cause she could-n't help_ me

(Verses 2 & 3. see block lyrics)

with my mind, peo-ple think I'm in - sane be - cause I___ am frown-ing

all the time.

Can you help_ me oc - cu - py___ my brain?_

Oh_____ yeah._

D.C. al Coda
(after repeat)

4. Make a joke and I___ will sigh_ and you___ will laugh and I___ will cry,

(Verse 5 see block lyrics)

hap - pi - ness_ I can - not feel and_ love___ to me_ is so un - real.

Verse 2:
All day long I think of things
But nothing seems to satisfy
Think I'll lose my mind
If I don't find something to pacify.

Verse 3:
I need someone to show me the things
In life that I can't find
I can't see the things that
Make true happiness, I must be blind.

Verse 5:
And so as you hear these words
Telling you now of my state
I tell you to enjoy life
I wish I could, but it's too late.

171

Peggy Sue

Words & Music by Buddy Holly, Norman Petty & Jerry Allison

© Copyright 1957 MPL Communications Incorporated, USA.
Peermusic (UK) Limited.
All Rights Reserved. International Copyright Secured.

If you knew____ Peg-gy Sue.____ Then you'd

(Verse 2 see block lyrics)

know why I feel blue____ a-bout Peg-gy,____ 'bout my

Peg-gy Sue.____ Oh, well, I love you gal;____

—— yes I love you, Peg-gy Sue.____

Peg-gy Sue.____ Peg-gy Sue.____ Pret-ty, pret-ty,

pret-ty, pret-ty, Peg-gy Sue!____ Oh, my Peg-gy,

Verse 2:
Peggy Sue, Peggy Sue
Oh, how my heart yearnd for you
Oh, Peggy, my Peggy Sue!

Pride (In The Name Of Love)

Words & Music by U2

© Copyright 1984 Blue Mountain Music Limited/Mother Music/Taiyo Music Incorporated/PolyGram International Music Publishing Limited.
All Rights Reserved. International Copyright Secured.

1. One man come in the name of love, one man come and go.___
(Verse 2 see block lyrics)

One man come he to jus - ti - fy, one man to ov - er - throw.___ In the name_

___ of love,___ what more___ in the name of_ love.___ In the name_

___ of love,___ what more___ in the name of love.___

Mm

Verse 2:
One man caught on a barbed-wire fence
One man he resist
One man washed on an empty beach
One man betrayed with a kiss.

175

Purple Rain

Words & Music by Prince

© Copyright 1984 Controversy Music, USA.
Universal/MCA Music Limited.
All rights in Germany administered by Universal/MCA Music Publ. GmbH.
All Rights Reserved. International Copyright Secured.

1. I nev-er meant 2 cause U___ an-y sor-row,
(Verse 2 see block lyrics)

I nev-er meant 2 cause___ U an-y pain.___

I on-ly want-ed one time 2 see U laugh-ing.___ I on-ly want-ed 2 see U laugh-ing

in the pur-ple___ rain. Pur-ple___rain, pur-ple rain.___ Pur-ple___ rain, pur-ple rain.___

___ Pur-ple___ rain, pur-ple rain.___ I on-ly want-ed 2 see U bath-ing
2° un-der

1.

in the pur-ple___ rain. 2. I nev-er want-ed 2 be your___ week-end___ lov-
- neath

176

Verse 2:
I never wanted 2 be your weekend lover
All I wanna be is some kind of friend
Baby I could never steal U from another
It's such a shame our friendship had 2 end.

Rikki Don't Lose That Number

Words & Music by Walter Becker & Donald Fagen

© Copyright 1974 MCA Music Publishing (a division of Universal Studios Incorporated), USA.
Universal/MCA Music Limited.
All rights in Germany administered by Universal/MCA Music Publ. GmbH.
All Rights Reserved. International Copyright Secured.

1. We hear you're leav-ing, that's O. K. I thought our lit-tle
(Verse 2 see block lyrics)

wild time had just be - gun. I guess you kind of scared your- self, you turn_

_ and run._ But if you have a change of heart._

Rik-ki don't lose that num - ber, you don't want to call no-bo - dy else._

Send it off in a let-ter to your - self. Rik-ki don't lose that num -

- ber, it's the on - ly one you own._ You might use it if you feel

Verse 2:
I have a friend in town, he's heard your name
We can go out driving on Slowhand Row
We could stay inside and play games, I don't know
And you could have a change of heart.

179

Rockin' All Over The World

Words & Music by John Fogerty

© Copyright 1975 Wenaha Music Company, USA.
Hornall Brothers Music Limited.
All Rights Reserved. International Copyright Secured.

Verse 2:
A giddy up and giddy up and get away
We're going crazy and we're going today
Here we go, rocking all over the world.

Verse 3:
I'm gonna tell your mama what you're gonna do
Come on out with your dancing shoes
Here we go, rocking all over the world.

181

Run To The Hills

Words & Music by Steve Harris

© Copyright 1982 Zomba Music Publishers Limited.
All Rights Reserved. International Copyright Secured.

White man came a-cross the sea__ he brought us__ pain__ and mi-se-ry.__ He killed our__ tribes he killed our__ creed,__ he took our game for his own need.__ We fought him__ hard__ we fought him__ well, out on the__ plains__ we gave him hell.__ But ma-ny came,__ too much for Cree,__ oh will we__ ev-er__ be set__ free?__

2. Run-ning through dust clouds and bar-ren wastes gal-lop-ing hard on the
(Verse 3 see block lyrics)

plains._ Chas-ing the red-skins back to their homes_

fight-ing them at their own game._ Mur-der for free-dom a

stab in the back wo-men and child-ren the cow-ards at-tack.____

Run to the hills. Run for_ your lives.____

Run to the hills. Run for your lives.____

lives.____

183

Verse 2:
Soldier Blue in the barren wastes
Hunting and killing's a game
Raping the women and wasting the men
The only good Indians are tame
Selling them whiskey and taking their gold
Enslaving the young and destroying the old.

184

Run

A song for which the word 'anthemic' might have been invented, 'Run' usually prompts emotional reactions to do with romantic separations or moments of personal loss. It was Snow Patrol's mainstream breakthrough single and no doubt provided the bitter-sweet soundtrack to many an affair in the spring of 2004. Snow Patrol's lead singer Gary Lightbody once rather shamefacedly admitted that he wrote it after falling down a flight of stairs drunk in Glasgow. The accident could easily have killed him and he wrote 'Run' soon afterwards using the phrase 'Light up, light up' to signify a light at the end of a tunnel. As an interpretation this might leave all those swaying, misty-eyed festival-goers feeling a little short-changed, but whatever the inspiration, it was an undeniably seductive song. In 2008 *X-Factor* winner Leona Lewis decided 'Run' was not dramatic enough and gave it the full Shirley Bassey treatment. Gary Lightbody said he liked it.

Run

Words & Music by Gary Lightbody, Jonathan Quinn, Mark McClelland, Nathan Connolly & Iain Archer

© Copyright 2003 Kobalt Music Publishing Limited (5%)/ Universal Music Publishing BL Limited (95%)
(administered in Germany by Universal Music Publ. GmbH).
All Rights Reserved. International Copyright Secured.

Loud-er, loud-er, and we'll run for our lives, I can hard-ly speak,I un
- der-stand why you can't raise your voice to say.

3. To think I Slow - er, slow-er we don't have time for that.
Have heart my dear, we're bound to be a-fraid,

All I want's to find an eas - ier way to get out of our lit-tle heads.
ev-en if it's just for a few days, mak-ing up for all this mess.

Light up, light up as if you have a choice,

ev-en if you can-not hear my voice, I'll be right be-side you dear.

Verse 3:
To think I might not see those eyes
Makes it so hard not to cry
And as we say our long goodbyes
I nearly do.

187

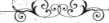

School's Out

Words & Music by Alice Cooper, Michael Bruce, Dennis Dunaway, Neal Smith & Glen Buxton

© Copyright 1972 Bizarre Music Incorporated & Ezra Music Corporation/Bizarre Music Incorporated, USA.
Carlin Music Corporation.
All Rights Reserved. International Copyright Secured.

D.C. al Coda

dir - ty looks.___

Coda

School's out for sum-mer. School's out for -

- ev-er.___ School's been blown to piec-es.

No more pen - cils, no more books.___ No more teach-ers' dir - ty looks.___
Out for sum-mer, out till fall.___ We might not go back at all.___

School's out for - ev-er. School's out for sum-mer.

School's out with fe-ver. School's out com - plete-ly.

Verse 2:
Well we got no class
And we got no principles
And we got no innocence
We can't even think of a word that rhymes.

189

See Emily Play

Words & Music by Syd Barrett

© Copyright 1967 Westminster Music Limited.
All Rights Reserved. International Copyright Secured.

E - mi - ly tries___ but mis - un - der - stands (Ah -
(Verses 2 & 3 see block lyrics)

- ah) She's of - ten in - clined to bor - row some - bo - dy's dreams till to -

-mor-row. There is no oth - er day. Let's try it an - oth - er way.

You'll lose your mind___ at play.___ Free

games for May. See_____ E - mi - ly play.

1, 2. G

3. G   D

Verse 2:
Soon after dark Emily cries (Ah-ah)
Gazing through trees in sorrow hardly a sound till tomorrow.

Verse 3:
Put on a gown that touches the ground (Ah-ah)
Float on a river for ever and ever Emily.

190

Shake, Rattle And Roll

Words & Music by Charles Calhoun

© Copyright 1954 Progressive Music Company Incorporated, USA.
Campbell Connelly & Company Limited.
All Rights Reserved. International Copyright Secured.

1. Get out_____ o' that kitch-en and rat-tle those pots and pans!_____ Get out_

(Verses 2-4 see block lyrics)

_____ o' that kitch-en and rat-tle those pots and pans!_____ Well,

roll my break-fast, 'cause_ I'm a hun-gry man!_____ I said, shake, rat-tle and roll!_____

_ I said, shake, rat-tle and roll!_____ I said, shake, rat-tle and roll!_____ I said,

shake, rat-tle and roll!___ You nev-er do noth-in' to save your dog-gone soul!

Verse 2:
You're wearing those dresses, your hair done up so nice *(x2)*
You look so warm but your heart is cold as ice.

Verse 3:
I'm like a one-eyed cat, peepin' in a sea-food store *(x2)*
I can look at you and tell you don't love me no more.

Verse 4:
I believe you're doing me wrong and now I know *(x2)*
The more I work, the faster my money goes.

191

She Bangs The Drums

Words & Music by John Squire & Ian Brown

© Copyright 1989 Zomba Music Publishers Limited.
All Rights Reserved. International Copyright Secured.

Verse 2:
I don't feel too steady on my feet
I feel hollow, I feel weak
Passion fruit and holy bread
Fill my guts and ease my head
Through the early morning sun
I can see her, here she comes
She bangs the drums.

Smells Like Teen Spirit

'Smells Like Teen Spirit' was a happy accident that no one in Seattle grunge band Nirvana thought would become their crossover hit. Released in September 1991 as the lead single from the album *Nevermind*, it was discovered and heavily played by campus and modern rock radio stations. The video received its world premiere late-night on MTV but before long was aired in the daytime too due to public demand. By January 1992 the album that featured it hit the No. 1 spot in the US charts. Kurt Cobain made no secret of the fact that the song was derivative of The Pixies. 'I was trying to write the ultimate pop song. I was basically trying to rip off the Pixies' he said. 'I should have been in that band' (Cobain's quotes nearly always started with the word 'I'). On the record his slurred delivery made the lyrics incomprehensible, but now you can see what they were.

Nirvana

Smells Like Teen Spirit

Words & Music by Kurt Cobain, Dave Grohl & Krist Novoselic

© Copyright 1991 EMI Music Publishing Limited (75%)/Universal/MCA Music Limited (12.5%)/Fintage Publishing And Collection (12.5%)
All rights in Germany administered by Universal/MCA Music Publ. GmbH.
All Rights Reserved. International Copyright Secured.

1.Load up on guns, bring your friends, it's fun to lose
(Verses 2 - 4 see block lyrics)

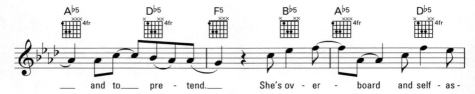

and to pre - tend. She's ov - er - board and self - as -

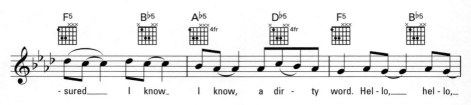

- sured I know I know, a dir - ty word. Hel - lo, hel - lo

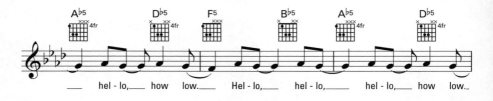

hel - lo, how low. Hel - lo, hel - lo, hel - lo, how low.

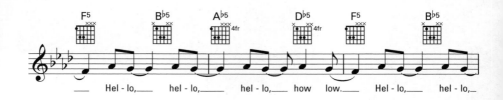

Hel - lo, hel - lo, hel - lo, how low. Hel - lo, hel - lo,

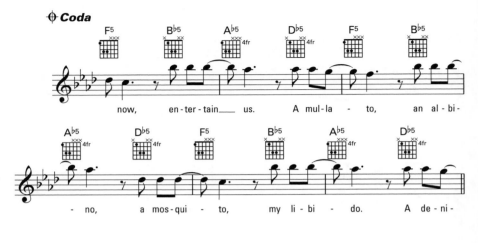

now, en - ter - tain___ us. A mul - la - to, an al - bi -

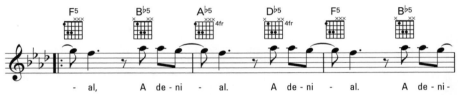

- no, a mos - qui - to, my li - bi - do. A de - ni -

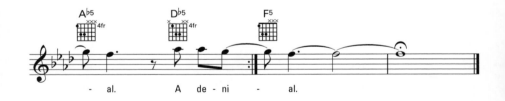

- al, A de - ni - al. A de - ni - al. A de - ni -

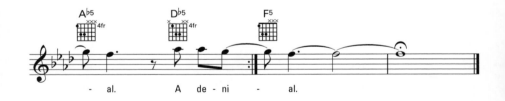

- al. A de - ni - al.

Verse 2:
I'm worse at what I do best
And for this gift I feel blessed
Our little group has always been
And always will until the end.

Verse 3: (Instrumental)

Verse 4:
And I forget just what it takes
And yeah, I guess, it makes me smile
I found it hard, it's hard to find
Oh well, whatever, nevermind.

Since You've Been Gone

Words & Music by Russ Ballard

© Copyright 1976 Russell Ballard Limited.
Complete Music Limited.
All Rights Reserved. International Copyright Secured.

I get the same old dreams, same time ev-'ry night, fall to the ground an' I
(Verse 2 see block lyrics)

wake up, so I get out of bed put on my shoes an' in my head

thoughts fly back to the break up, these four walls are clo -

- sin' in. Look at the fix you've put me in.

Since you've been gone, since you've been gone, I'm out of my head, can't take

it. Could I be wrong, but since you've been gone

Could I be wrong,— but since you've been— gone,—

you cast a spell— so— break it.—

Oh,— oh,—

oh,— oh,—

ev - er since you've been gone.—

Verse 2:
So in the night I stand beneath the back-street light
I read the words that you sent to me
I could take the afternoon but night-time comes around too soon
You can't know what you mean to me
Your poison letter, your telegram
Just goes to show you don't give a damn.

Somebody To Love

Words & Music by Darby Slick

© Copyright 1967 Copperpenny Music, USA/Irving Music Corporation, USA.
Universal Music Publishing Limited.
All rights in Germany administered by Universal Music Publ. GmbH.
All Rights Reserved. International Copyright Secured.

1. When the truth is found to be lies, and
(Verses 2 & 4 see block lyrics)

all the joy with-in you dies... Don't you

want some-bod-y to love? Don't you need some-bod-y to love?

Would-n't you love some-bod-y to love? You'd bet-ter find

1.
some-bod-y to love. (ad lib. Gtr. solo)

2.
2. When the some-bo-dy to love. 3. Your eyes, I say your eyes

202

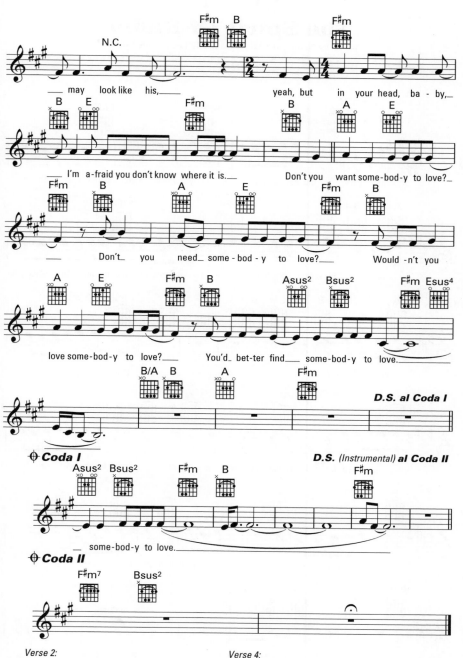

Verse 2:
When the garden flow'rs they are dead
Yes and your mind, your mind, is so full of red
Don't you want somebody to love?

Verse 4:
Tears are running, they're all running down your breast
And your friends baby, they treat you like a guest
Don't you want somebody to love?

The Spirit Of Radio

Words by Neil Peart • Music by Geddy Lee & Alex Lifeson

© Copyright 1980 Core Music Publishing Company, Canada.
Carlin Music Corporation.
All Rights Reserved. International Copyright Secured.

-te-gri-ty,— yeah.

In - vi - si - ble air - ways crack-le with life,—

bright an - ten - nae bris - tle with the en - er - gy.

E - mo-tion-al feed-back on a time-less wave-length, bear-ing a gift— be-yond

price: al - most— free.

For the words of the pro-fits were writ-ten on the stu-di-o wall,

con-cert hall and

ech-oes with the sound of sales - men, of sales - men, of sales -

- men!

Strutter

Words & Music by Paul Stanley & Gene Simmons

© Copyright 1974 Hori Productions America Incorporated/Cafe Americana/Gladwyne Music Publishing Corporation, USA.
Universal Music Publishing Limited.
All rights in Germany administered by Universal Music Publ. GmbH.
All Rights Reserved. International Copyright Secured.

1. I know a thing or two a-bout her.
(Verse 2 see block lyrics)

I know she'll on-ly make you cry.

She'll let you walk the street be-side her. Ooh.

But when she walks she'll pass you by.

Ev-'ry-bo-dy says she's look-in' good,

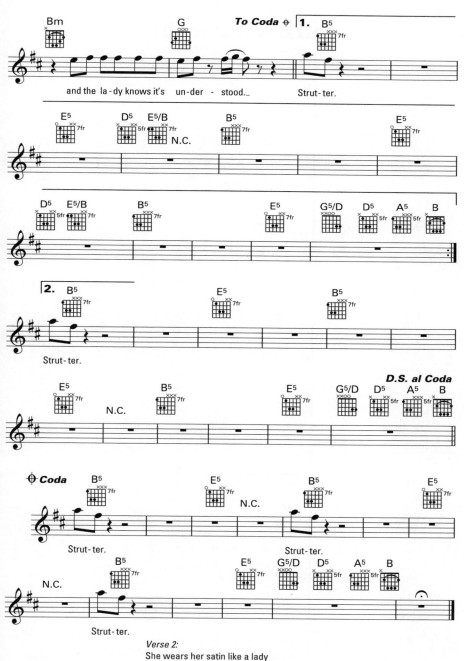

and the la-dy knows it's un-der - stood.— Strut-ter.

Strut-ter.

Strut-ter.

Strut-ter.

Strut-ter.

Strut-ter.

Verse 2:
She wears her satin like a lady
She gets her way just like a child
You take her home and she says, "Maybe, baby."
She takes you down and drives you wild.

Suffragette City

Words & Music by David Bowie

© Copyright 1972 Tintoretto Music/RZO Music Limited (37.5%)/EMI Music Publishing Limited (37.5%)/Chrysalis Music Limited, (25%).
All Rights Reserved. International Copyright Secured.

210

oh,___ she's al - right. A Suf-fra-gette Ci - ty.

A Suf-fra-gette Ci - ty. I'm back on Suf-fra-gette Ci -

- ty. I'm back on Suf-fra-gette Ci - ty. A Suf-fra-gette Ci-

- ty. A Suf-fra-gette Ci - ty. A Suf-fra-gette Ci-

- ty. A Suf-fra-gette.

1. *Repeat ad lib.*

Oh,___ wham bam thank-you Mam! Suf-fra-gette.

Verse 3:
Hey man, oh Henry don't be unkind, go away
Hey man, I can't take you this time, no way
Hey man, say Droogie don't crash here
There's only room for one and here she comes, here she comes.

Sultans Of Swing

Words & Music by Mark Knopfler

© Copyright 1978 Straitjacket Songs Limited.
All Rights Reserved. International Copyright Secured.

trum-pet play-ing band,_____ it ain't what they call rock and roll._

(Guitar) And the Sul - tans,

Yeah, the Sul - tans_ are play-ing Cre-ole.

Cre - ole ba - by.

D.S. al Coda

Ah, ah.

Coda

Repeat to fade

swing._

Verse 3:
You check out Guitar George
He knows all the chords
Mind, he's strictly rhythm,
He doesn't want to make it cry or sing
When he gets up under the lights to play his thing.

Verse 4:
And Harry doesn't mind if he doesn't make the scene
He's got a daytime job he's doing alright
He can play the honky-tonk just like anything
Saving it up, Friday night sound
With the Sultans, with the Sultans of swing.

Verse 6:
And then the man he steps right up to the microphone
And says at last
Just as the time bell rings
"Goodnight, now it's time to go home."
And he makes it fast with one more thing
We are the Sultans
We are the Sultans of swing.

215

Summer Of '69

Words & Music by Bryan Adams & Jim Vallance

© Copyright 1984 Almo Music Corporation/Adams Communications Incorporated/Testatyme Music/Irving Music Corporation, USA.
Rondor Music (London) Limited.
All rights in Germany administered by Rondor Musikverlag GmbH.
All Rights Reserved. International Copyright Secured.

I got my first real six-string, bought it at the five and dime.

Played it 'til my fin-gers bled, was the sum-mer of six-ty nine.

1. Me and some guys from school had a band and we tried real hard.
(Verses 2 & 3 see block lyrics)

Jim-my quit and Jo-dy got mar-ried. I should-a known we'd nev-er get far.

Oh, when I look back now, that sum-mer seemed to last for - ev - er,

and if I had the choice, yeah, I'd al-ways wan-na be there.

Those— were the best days of my— life.

Back in the sum-mer of six - ty nine.—

Man,— we were kill - in' time,— we were young and rest - less, we

need - ed to—— un - wind. I guess noth - in' can last— for - ev -

- er, for ev - er,—— no!

Back in the sum-mer of six-ty nine.— Back in the sum-mer of

Verse 2:
Ain't no use complainin' when you got a job to do
Spent my evenin's down at the drive-in, and that's when I met you
Standin' on your mama's porch, you told me that you'd wait forever
Oh, and when you held my hand, I knew that it was now or never
Those were the best days of my life.

Verse 3:
And now the times are changin', look at everything that's come and gone
Sometimes when I play that old six-string I think about you, wonder what went wrong
Standin' on your mama's porch, you told me it'd last forever
Oh, and when you held my hand, I knew that it was now or never
Those were the best days of my life.

Sunshine Of Your Love

Words & Music by Jack Bruce, Pete Brown & Eric Clapton

© Copyright 1967 & 1996 Warner/Chappell Music Limited (66.66%)/Eric Clapton (33.34%).
All Rights Reserved. International Copyright Secured.

218

Verse 2:
I'm with you love
The light's shining through on you
Yes, I'm with you my love
It's the morning and just we two
I'll stay with you, darling, now
I'll be with you 'til my seeds are dried up.

Teach Your Children

Words & Music by Graham Nash

© Copyright 1970 Nashnotes, USA.
Sony/ATV Music Publishing (UK) Limited.
All Rights Reserved. International Copyright Secured.

Verse 2:
And you of tender years
Can't know the fears that your elders grew by
And so please help them with your youth
They seek the truth before they can die
Teach your parents well
Their children's hell will slowly go by.

Teenage Kicks

What is there left to say about the legendary 'Teenage Kicks' except that it was one of those rare moments where everything went right – a potent distillation of The Undertones' fleeting brand of punkish power pop elevated to unlikely fame by an influential DJ's obsession. History records that John Peel championed the Derry lads from the start, paid for their first recording session and remained an emotional slave to 'Teenage Kicks' for the remainder of his life. Quite apart from that – and the song's relatively modest 1978 chart success – 'Teenage Kicks' really was a great three-chord rallying cry for youth. It has since been covered by numerous artists including Buzzcocks, K.T. Tunstall and Snow Patrol.

Teenage Kicks

Words & Music by John O'Neill

© Copyright 1978 West Bank Songs Limited.
Universal/MCA Music Limited.
All rights in Germany administered by Universal/MCA Music Publ. GmbH.
All Rights Reserved. International Copyright Secured.

224

I need ex-cite-ment, oh, I need it bad___ and she's the best I've

ev - er had.___ I wan - na hold her, wan - na

hold her tight, get teen-age kicks___ right through the night.___ Al- right!

I wan-na hold her wan-na hold her tight get teen-age kicks___ right

through the night.___

Time Is Running Out

Words & Music by Matthew Bellamy, Chris Wolstenholme & Dominic Howard

© Copyright 2003 Taste Music Limited.
All Rights Reserved. International Copyright Secured.

murder it. And our time is running out, and our time is

running out, you can't push it underground, you can't stop it screaming out.

2. I wanted freedom, bound and restricted,

I tried to give you up,— but I'm addicted. Now that you know I'm trapped, sense of elation,

you'll never dream of— breaking this fixation. You will squeeze athe

life— out of— me.— And bury it, I won't let— you

bury it, I won't let— you smother it, I won't let— you murder it.

Tumbling Dice

Words & Music by Mick Jagger & Keith Richards

© Copyright 1972 Promopub B.V., Holland.
Westminster Music Limited.
All Rights Reserved. International Copyright Secured.

Wom - en think I'm tast - y, but they're al - ways try - in' to waste me and make __ me burn the can - dle right down, __ but ba - by, __ ba - by, __ I don't need no jewels __ in my crown. __ 'Cause all __ you wo - men is low - down __ gam - blers, cheat - in' like I don't know how, __ but ba - by, __ ba - by, __ there's fe - ver in the funk house now. __ This low down bitch - in' got my __ poor feet a - itch - in', you know, __ you know the deuce is still wild. __

229

call me the tum - blin',_ roll_____ me and call me the tum - blin'_

dice._____ Oh, my,_____ my, my,___ I'm the lone

___ crap shoot - er, play - in' the field___ ev - 'ry night._____

Ba - by,___ can't stay,_ you got to roll_____ me and

call me the tum - blin'____ roll_____ me and
(dice.)_____

call me the tum - blin',___ dice._____

Repeat to fade

Got to roll me, got to

Tutti Frutti

Words & Music by Richard Penniman, Dorothy La Bostrie & Joe Lubin

© Copyright 1955 Venice Music Corporation, USA.
Sony/ATV Music Publishing (UK) Limited.
All Rights Reserved. International Copyright Secured.

232

Verse 2:
I got a gal, her name's Daisy
She almost drives me crazy
I got a gal, her names's Daisy
She almost drives me crazy
She's a real gone cookie, yes siree
But pretty little Suzy's the gal for me.

20th Century Boy

Marc Bolan's sparkly glam-rock career was beginning to decline in 1973 when the self-penned '20th Century Boy' took T-Rex to No. 3 in the UK charts. It was to prove a durable song and its popularity would outlive its author. Bolan died in a car crash in 1977 shortly before his 30th birthday but '20th Century Boy' became a hit all over again in 1991 when it was one of the songs co-opted by Levi's for a famous series of TV commercials. It was featured in the ad where a young Brad Pitt finds his prized Levi's are conspicuously missing from a box of returned possessions as he is released from a Mexican jail. Happily the leggy brunette who drives up in the dust to collect him has brought a spare pair as well as herself as consolation prizes.

20th Century Boy

Words & Music by Marc Bolan

© Copyright 1973 Wizard (Bahamas) Limited.
All Rights Reserved. International Copyright Secured.

♩ = 134

1. Friends___ say it's fine, friends___ say it's good, ev-
(Verses 2 & 3 see block lyrics)

-'ry-bod-y says it's just___ like rock 'n' roll___ (Ah.)___

I move___ like a cat, charge___

___ like a ram, sting___ like a bee, babe,___ I wan-na be your man.___

(Ah.)___

To Coda ⊕

Well it's plain___

1.

___ to see___ you re-mem - ber___ me,___ yeah, I'm___ your boy,___ your twen-ti-eth

235

Verse 2:
Friends say it's fine, friends say it's good
Everybody says it's just like rock 'n' roll
Fly like a plane, drive like a car
Ball like a hound, babe I wanna be your man
Well it's plain to see you were meant for me
I'm your toy, your twentieth century boy.

Verse 3:
Friends say it's fine, friends say it's good
Everybody says it's just like rock 'n' roll
I move like a cat, charge like a ram
Sting like a bee, babe I wanna be your man
Well it's plain to see you were meant for me
Yeah, I'm your toy, your twentieth century boy.

Use Somebody

This huge hit from Kings Of Leon epitomises the band's rise from alternative darlings to unashamed stadium rockers. Written in Glasgow in 2007 in response to a falling out within the band while on tour, it entered the UK singles chart at number 29 in September 2008 thanks to download sales alone. Its physical release in December gave it a mighty rersurgence and thereafter 'Use Somebody' was a long-term charting single in the UK spending some 40 weeks in the top 75. Chart success in the US followed. In their more charitable moments the Nashville band credit the UK with launching their career, but even so they showed a more hostile response to the audience at the 2009 Reading Festival whom they thought to be insufficiently admiring. In any case the song's parent album *Only By The Night* would go on to be one of the biggest-sellers of the year.

Use Somebody

Words & Music by Caleb Followill, Nathan Followill, Jared Followill & Matthew Followill

© Copyright 2008 Martha Street Music/Followill Music/McFearless Music/Coffee Tea Or Me Publishing.
Bug Music Limited (45%)/P & P Songs Limited (55%).
All Rights Reserved. International Copyright Secured.

1. I've been roam-ing a - round, al-ways look-ing down at all I see.

(Verses 2 & 3 see block lyrics)

Paint-ed fac - es fill the plac - es I can't reach.

You know that I could use some - bod - y.

You know that I could

1. use some - bo - dy. 2. Some-one like you

2. Some - one like you. Oh, oh.

Some-one like you.___ Some-bo - dy.___

Some-one like you.___ Some bo - dy.___ Some-one like you.___

___ Some-bo - dy.___ I've been roam-ing a - round,___

___ al-ways look-ing down___ at all___ I see.___

Verse 2:
Someone like you and all you know and how you speak
Countless lovers, undercover of the street
You know that I could use somebody
You know that I could use somebody.

Verse 3:
Off in the night while you live it up, I'm off to sleep
Waging wars to shake the poet and the beat
I hope it's gonna make you notice
I hope it's gonna make you notice.

Waterloo Sunset

Words & Music by Ray Davies

© Copyright 1967 Davray Music Limited.
Carlin Music Corporation.
All Rights Reserved. International Copyright Secured.

Original key: E♭. To match original recording, use a capo, 1st fret.

1. Dir - ty old riv - er must you keep roll - ing flow-ing in - to
(Verses 2 & 3 see block lyrics)

__ the night, __ Peo - ple so bu - sy, make me feel diz -

- zy, ta - xi lights shine __ so bright. But I don't __

__ need no friends __ As long as I gaze __

__ on Wa-ter-loo sun - set, I am in par - ra - dise.

Ev -'ry day I look at the world from my win - dow.

The chil - ly, chil - li - est eve - ning time.___ Wat - er - loo sun - set's fine.

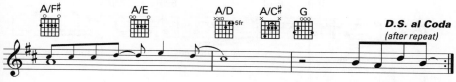

(Wat - er - loo sun - set's fine.)___

2. Ter - ry meets Ju -

- set they are in pa - ra - dise.

Guitar solo

Wat - er - loo sun - set's fine.___

(Wat - er - loo sun - set's fine.)___

Verse 2:
Terry meets Julie, Waterloo Station, every Friday night
But I'm so lazy, don't want to wander, I stay at home at night
But I don't feel afraid
As long as I gaze on Waterloo sunset
I am in paradise.

Verse 3:
Millions of people, swarming like flies 'round Waterloo underground
Terry and Julie cross over the river, where they feel safe and sound
And they don't need no friends
As long as they gaze on Waterloo sunset
They are in paradise.

243

We've Got Tonight

Words & Music by Bob Seger

© Copyright 1978 Gear Publishing Company Incorporated, USA.
Minder Music Limited.
All Rights Reserved. International Copyright Secured.

♩ = 80

1. I know it's late,_____ I know you're wea - ry. I know your plans_
(Verse 2 see block lyrics)

___ don't in-clude me.__ Still here we are____ both of us lone -

- ly, long-ing for shel - ter from all that we see.__ Why should we wor-

- ry, no - one will care,___ girl. Look at the stars_

___ so far a-way._____ We've got to - night___ who needs to-mor -

1.

- row? We've got to-night__ babe,__ why don't you stay? 2. Deep in my soul,

245

Verse 2:
Deep in my soul I've been so lonely
All of my hopes fading away
I've longed for love like everyone else does
I know I'll keep searching even after today
So there it is, girl, I've said it all now
And here we are, babe, what do you say?

What's Up?

Words & Music by Linda Perry

© Copyright 1993 Famous Music Corporation, USA.
All Rights Reserved. International Copyright Secured.

Twen-ty-five years and my life is still___ try-ing to get up___ that great big hill___ of___ hope___ for a des-ti-na - tion. I re-a-lised quick - ly when I knew I should that the world_____ was made up of this broth-er - hood___ of___ man,___ for what-ev-er that means.___ And so I cry some-times when I'm ly-ing in bed___ just to get it all out___ what's in___ my head and I,___ I am feel-ing a lit-tle pe-cu - liar. And so I

247

249

When You Were Young

Words & Music by Brandon Flowers, Dave Keuning, Mark Stoermer & Ronnie Vannucci

© Copyright 2006 Universal Music Publishing Limited.
All rights in Germany administered by Universal Music Publ. GmbH.
All Rights Reserved. International Copyright Secured.

(Talks like a gen-tle-man. Like you i-ma-gined.) When you

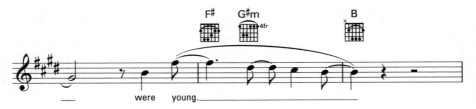

were young.

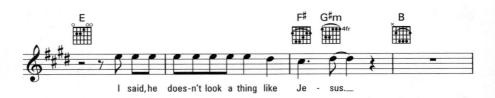

I said, he does-n't look a thing like Je - sus.

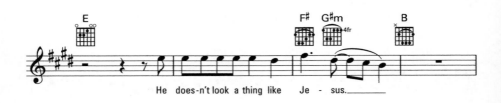

He does-n't look a thing like Je - sus.

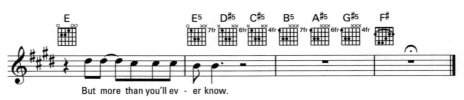

But more than you'll ev - er know.

Verse 2:
Can we climb this mountain?
I don't know
Higher now than ever before
I know we can make it if we take it slow
Let's take it easy
Easy now, watch it go
We're burning down the highway
Skyline on the back of a hurricane
That started turning when you were young.

White Wedding

Words & Music by Billy Idol

© Copyright 1982 Boneidol Music/Rare Blue Music Incorporated, USA.
Chrysalis Music Limited.
All Rights Reserved. International Copyright Secured.

1, 3. Hey lit-tle sis-ter, what__ have you__ done?

(Verse 2 see block lyrics)

Hey lit-tle sis-ter, who's__ the on - ly one?

Hey lit-tle sis-ter, who's__ your su - per-man? Hey lit-tle sis-ter, who's__

__ the one__ we want? Hey lit-tle sis-ter, shot - gun! It's a nice day to

start__ a-gain.__ It's a nice day for a

white wed-ding. It's a nice day to

start__ a - gain.

start__ a - gain._____

I've been a-way for so_____ long, (so__ long.) I've been a-way for so_

__ long, (so__ long.) I let you go for so_____ long,   It's a   nice day to

start__ a - gain.__   It's a   nice day for a

254

white wed-ding. It's a nice day to start a-gain.

There is no-thing fair in this world,

There is no-thing safe in this world. And there's

no-thing sure in this world, and there's no-thing pure in this world, look for

some-thing left in this world. Start a-gain.

come on, it's a nice day for a white wed-ding.

It's a nice day to start a-gain. It's a

Verse 2:
Hey little sister, who is it you're with?
Hey little sister, what's your vice and wish?
Hey little sister, shotgun, oh yeah
Hey little sister, who's your superman?

Wind Of Change

Words & Music by Klaus Meine

© Copyright 1990 PRI Music Incorporated, USA.
Universal Music Publishing Limited.
All rights in Germany administered by Universal Music Publ. GmbH.
All Rights Reserved. International Copyright Secured.

1. I fol-low the Mos-kva down to Gor-ky Park,___ list-'nin' to the wind of change.___ Au-gust sum-mer night, sol-diers pass-ing by ___ list-'nin' to the wind of change.___

Whistle

2. The world is clos-ing in, and did you ev-er think___ that we could be so close like bro - thers.

(Verse 3 see block lyrics)

The fu-ture's in the air, I can feel it ev-'ry-where,___

256

blow-ing with the wind of change.___ Take me to the

ma-gic of the mo-ment, on a glo - ry night__ where the child-ren of to-mor-row dream a -

1.
- way____ in the wind of change.

2.
me.

Take me to the ma-gic of the mo-ment on a glo - ry night__ where the

chil-dren of to-mor-row dream a - way_____ in the wind of change.

The wind of change blows straight in-to the face of time, like a storm wind that will

ring____ the free-dom bell for peace of mind let___ your ba-la-lai-ka

sing what my gui-tar,__ wants to sing.

Take me to the ma-gic of the mo-ment, on a glo - ry night__ where the

chil-dren of to-mor-row share their dreams_____ with you and me.

Take me to the mag-ic of the mo-ment, on a glo - ry night__ where the

chil-dren of to-mor-row dream a - way_____ in the wind of change.

rall.

a tempo rit.

Whistle

Verse 3:
Walking down the street
Distant memories are buried in the past forever
I follow the Moskva down to Gorky Park listenin' to the wind of change
Take me to the magic of the moment
On a glory night where the children of tomorrow share their dreams with you and me.

Wouldn't It Be Nice

Words & Music by Mike Love, Brian Wilson & Tony Asher

© Copyright 1966 Sea Of Tunes Publishing Company, USA.
Universal Music Publishing Limited.
All rights in Germany administered by Universal Music Publ. GmbH.
All Rights Reserved. International Copyright Secured.

(Verse 2 see block lyrics)

1. Would - n't it be nice if we were old - er, then we would - n't have to wait so long, and would-n't it be nice to live to - ge - ther in the kind of world where we be - long? You know, it's gon - na make it that much bet - ter when we can say good - night, and

1.

stay to - ge - ther. 2. Would - n't it be

Verse 2:
Wouldn't it be nice if we would wake up
In the morning when the day is new
And after having spent the day together
Hold each other close the whole night through?
The happy times together we've been spending
I wish that every kiss was never ending.

Wonderful Tonight

Words & Music by Eric Clapton

© Copyright 1977, 1999 & 2004 Eric Clapton.
All Rights Reserved. International Copyright Secured.

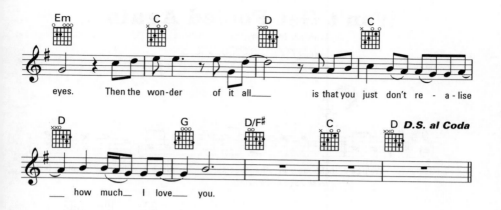

eyes.   Then the won-der   of it all___   is that you just don't re - a - lise

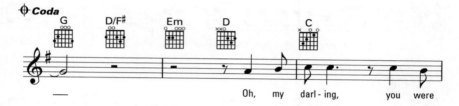

___ how much___ I love___ you.

___   Oh,   my   darl - ing,   you were

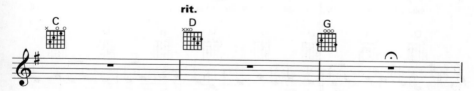

won - der - ful___   to - night."___

Verse 2:
We go to a party, and ev'ryone turns to see
This beautiful lady is walking around with me
And then she asks me, "Do you feel all right?"
And I say "Yes, I feel wonderful tonight."

Verse 3:
It's time to go home now, and I've got an aching head
So I give her the car keys, and she helps me to bed
And then I tell her, as I turn out the light
I say, "My darling, you were wonderful tonight."

Won't Get Fooled Again

Words & Music by Pete Townshend

© Copyright 1971 Fabulous Music Limited.
All Rights Reserved. International Copyright Secured.

We'll be fight-ing in the streets___ with our child-ren at our feet_
(Verse 2 see block lyrics)

___ and the mor-als that they wor - ship will be gone.___ And the

men who spurred us on___ sit in judge-ment of all wrong,___ they de-

-cide and a shot - gun sings the song.___ I'll

tip my hat___ to the new con-sti-tu - tion; take a bow___ for the new re-vo-lu - tion;

smile and grin___ at the change all a - round; pick up my gui-tar and play,___

Verse 2:
There's nothing in the street looks any different to me
And the slogans are replaced, by the by
The parting on the left is now a parting on the right
And the beards have all grown longer overnight.

You Took The Words
Right Out Of My Mouth
(Hot Summer Night)

Words & Music by Jim Steinman

© Copyright 1977 Edward B. Marks Music Company, USA. Carlin Music Corporation.
All Rights Reserved. International Copyright Secured.

♩ = 126

1. It was a hot sum-mer night_ and the beach_ was burn-ing. There was

(Verses 2 & 3 see block lyrics)

fog crawl-ing ov-er the sand._____ When I

lis-ten to your heart I hear the whole world turn - ing, I

1.
To Coda ⊕

see the shoot-ing stars fall-ing through your trem-bling hands.

2.

2. While you were not an-oth-er mo-ment, not___ an-oth-er mo-ment, not_

___ an-oth-er mo-ment to___ waste. Oh well, you

hold me so__ close_ that my knees__ grow weak,_ and my soul is fly - ing high a-

-bove the ground._ I'm try-ing to speak,_ but no mat-ter what I do I

just can't seem to make a - ny sound._ And then you

took the words right out of my mouth;__ oh, it

must have been while you were kiss - ing me._____ You

took the words right out of my mouth;__ oh, and I

swear it's true: I was just a - bout to say I love_____ you._

Verse 2:
While you were licking your lips and your lipstick shining
I was dying just to ask for a taste
Oh, we were lying together in a silver lining
By the light of the moon.

Verse 3:
Now my body is shaking like a wave on the water
And I guess that I'm begining to grin
Oh we're finally alone and we can do what we want to
Ooh the night is young.

You Ain't Seen Nothing Yet

Words & Music by Randy Bachman

© Copyright 1974 Ranbach Music, Canada.
Sony/ATV Music Publishing (UK) Limited.
All Rights Reserved. International Copyright Secured.

B - b - b - ba - by, you just ain't_____ seen - n - n - noth-ing yet.

Here's some-thing that you're nev - er gon - na for - get._____

B - b - b - ba - by, you just ain't_____ seen - n - n - no-thing yet.

To Coda ⊕ **1.**

No-thing yet, you ain't been a-round.
2° Spoken: (You need educating)

2.

2. And   *Spoken:* Got-ta

go to school.

D.S. al Coda

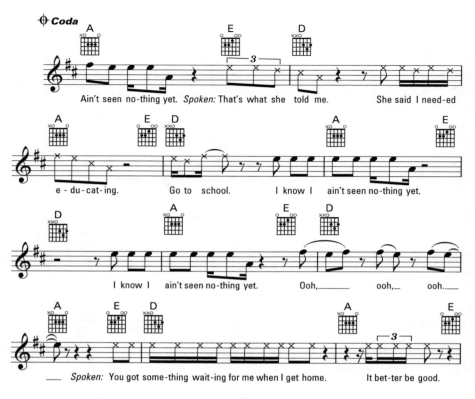

Ain't seen no-thing yet. *Spoken:* That's what she told me. She said I need-ed

e - du - cat - ing. Go to school. I know I ain't seen no-thing yet.

I know I ain't seen no-thing yet. Ooh,_____ ooh,_ ooh._

_ *Spoken:* You got some-thing wait-ing for me when I get home. It bet-ter be good.

I've been ev-ery- where, but I ain't seen no-thing yet.

Verse 2:
And now I'm feeling better
'Cause I found out for sure
She took me to her doctor
And he told me I was cured
He said that any love is good love
So I took what I could get
Yes I took what I could get
And then she looked at me
With her big brown eyes.

On %:

He said that any love is good love
So I took what I could get
Yes I took what I could get
And then she looked at me
With her big brown eyes.

123456789

272